Wild about Toton

A collection of observations of the flora and fauna, taken in Toton, Nottinghamshire

bats, butterflies, fish, fungi, insects, mosses, mammals, moths, plants, shrubs & trees

Collected by Friends of Toton Fields

Edited by Gillian E Morral

Whilst every care has been taken to ensure the accuracy of the information contained in this book, the authors cannot accept responsibility for any error or omission. The data collected has been recorded by volunteers, local residents and experts. By the nature of the movement of animals and birds, and other factors such as the changing seasons, the recording has not been continuous. It is therefore likely that other species may be present that have not been noted in this book.

This book has been written with every good intention, to 'put Toton on the map', to note the changes, to encourage others to explore and record and understand our area a little more.

Published by

Gillian E Morral

Copyright Friends of Toton Fields 2018

Printed by

MOORLEYS
Print, Design & Publishing
info@moorleys.co.uk · www.moorleys.co.uk

FSC
www.fsc.org
MIX
From responsible sources
FSC® C023367

Woodland
CARBON
www.woodlandcarbon.co.uk

Printed on Woodland Trust Paper

ISBN 978-0-9574853-1-0

Foreword

This book aims to combine Ainslie Carruthers' study of one year in the natural world around Toton, with further wildlife records collected by Friends of Toton Fields, in the local area close to Derbyshire in the south west of Nottinghamshire. From observing wildlife over a period of years, changes have been noted; with some species lost, and some gained. It is hoped that this book will record some of "Wild" Toton before it is lost to "progress", which appears to be the creation of more houses and the arrival of HS2 and therefore more concrete and urbanisation of an area once a highly agricultural area and rich in wildlife.

Acknowledgements

We (Friends of Toton Fields) would like to thank all local residents who have contributed to this book, in any way and particularly to Ainslie Carruthers. This book would not have happened at all without Ainslie, who wrote his diary in 2005 and subsequently founded Friends of Toton Fields. We would also like to thank Norman Lewis for his unswerving care, giving up his time and energy over many, many years to protect and, improve the conditions of the area for the human population and animal and plant species.

photo courtesy A.Heath

Norman Lewis MBE   **Ainslie Carruthers**

We would also like to especially thank the following for their various contributions:

Marion Bryce, Alan Heath and LENS- Long Eaton Naturalists
Adrian Orrell - Nottinghamshire Bat Association
Dr Sheila Wright - Nottinghamshire Larger Moth Recorder, & Curator of Natural Sciences (Biology) at Nottingham Natural History Museum
Margaret Crittenden - British Bryological Society Vice-county Recorder for Nottinghamshire
Rob Johnson NBGRC- Nottinghamshire Biological & Geographical Record centre
Lee Scudder- Countryside Officer Nottinghamshire County Council
Brian Wetton
Brian Parkes,
Peter & Jane Klymowskyj
Karen Barker, Graham Heal, Julie & Dave Bullock, Paul Carruthers & members of Friends of Toton Fields

Contents

Introduction

The wildlife study in this book focuses mainly on observations and recordings in and around Toton Fields Local Nature Reserve; although many species can also be seen in gardens and other open spaces in the area. Data has also been collected from the Local Nature Reserve(LNR) & Local Wildlife Site(LWS) which was formerly part of the Marshalling Yards at Toton Sidings.

Toton Fields Local Nature Reserve, established in 2009, is an area of mixed habitats. It is managed by Broxtowe Borough Council. Friends of Toton Fields act as an advisory body and help with such management activities as litter picks, care and maintenance of nest boxes etc. The site lies alongside the River Erewash with associated wetland species, wet grassland and young woodland. It is characterised by amenity grassland, hedgerow, parkland, small areas of mixed woodland (oak, ash, willow, poplar) scrub habitats and open water (River Erewash and created ponds). It is open to the public with numerous access points along the A6005 Nottingham Road, B6003 with unlimited access from the adjoining housing estates. There are two well maintained bridges across the River Erewash, which allows public access on to an area of land in between the River Erewash and the By Pass channel. There are numerous paths throughout the site.

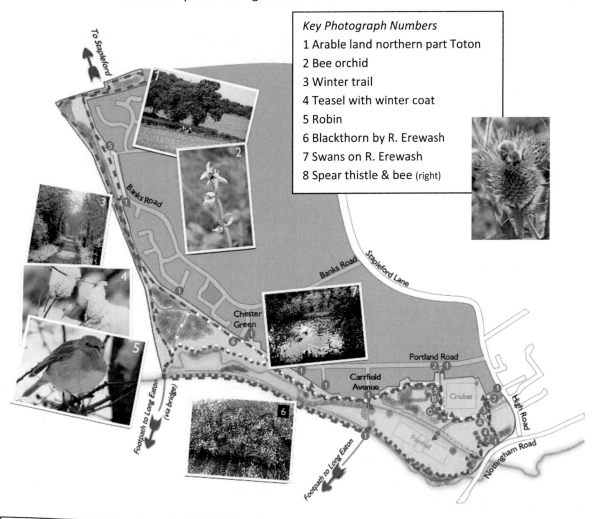

Key Photograph Numbers
1 Arable land northern part Toton
2 Bee orchid
3 Winter trail
4 Teasel with winter coat
5 Robin
6 Blackthorn by R. Erewash
7 Swans on R. Erewash
8 Spear thistle & bee (right)

Key to number on map
1 Entrances   2 Parking
3 Sports pavilion 4 Tennis Courts
5 Kids Play area 6 Greenwood centre

Map and info from leaflet produced by Friends of Toton Fields

Toton Fields Local Nature Reserve is a linear site which is 30 metres above sea level at its lowest point rising to 66 metres at the northern boundary. It is adjacent to the Toton Sidings – the marshalling yards which were once the largest in Europe. Housing developments in the 1960s and 80s have created a large estate on the eastern side.

The name Toton Fields relates to a farm called Toton Fields Farm which was situated on the site of the current Greenwood centre. Toton up to the mid 20th century was a rural, agricultural area with few houses and roads. Farm barns were home to bats, owls and other species. With a changing landscape from green to brown it is time to conserve and provide homes for homo sapiens (us) and the wildlife that exists in the area. This wildlife does indeed enhance our lives and brings joy (usually) when seen.

Geology and Soils

In the lower section of the nature reserve, the clays and loams of the floodplain indicates the presence of wet flood meadows and wet carr woodlands in old river meanders[1] while the soil on the higher land adjacent to the housing estates is shallow and coarse lying over red marl with beds of sandstone containing some gypsum. These soils tend to be heavy and poorly draining supporting typical Nottinghamshire plant communities. The soils have arisen from two main rock types – Alluvium deposits in the valley and Mercian Mudstone above these. At the highest point of the site the red marl is overlain by Glacial Till (Boulder clay)[2] which is a remnant of the ice age.

Recent activity

Following the writing of Ainslie's diary and the formation of Friends of Toton Fields group, much work has been done to improve and conserve the opportunities for wildlife. In 2015 ponds were created by the Environment Agency to attract invertebrates and amphibians. Hedge laying has been carried out in partnership with People's Conservation Volunteers (formerly the BTCV) in recent years, to maintain hedges as habitats for birds and other creatures.

There has been a concerted effort to record the wildlife in Toton with an emphasis on the lesser known species which occur often in abundance such as mosses. Volunteers and experts have spent many hours watching, catching & recording moths. There were some notable species recorded which are rarities in the county and of national importance. Some species while not rare had not been recorded here before. There is now a fairly comprehensive record of moths, butterflies,

flowers, birds, mosses, bats, and other small mammals which has been completed before the incursion of more housing and the proposed HS2 High Speed rail hub which will affect the landscape and the wildlife which inhabit Toton.

Changing seasons and changing climate bring variations in the wildlife. This book aims to give information on the current wildlife in Toton.

Left - Bargeman's cabbage found alongside canals or rivers is thought to have been used as a vegetable for Bargemen and their families. Other names include wild turnip.

[1] Toton Fields Local Nature Management Plan 2017
[2] Geological survey England & Wales 1910 Nottingham District sheet nos 125,126, 141, 146

Compartments /Habitats of the Local Nature Reserve

River Erewash

Toton Fields Local Nature Reserve has a range of habitats through which the River Erewash and the By Pass Channel flow. The present watercourses have evolved with human intervention over the centuries but particularly in the 20th century when a flood alleviation scheme was put in place. The River Erewash (wandering river) was the power for the water mill and in times gone by a channel (leat) was created to take water to the water mill which once stood near the present ball court in the Recreation Ground. An information board now marks the site of the mill.

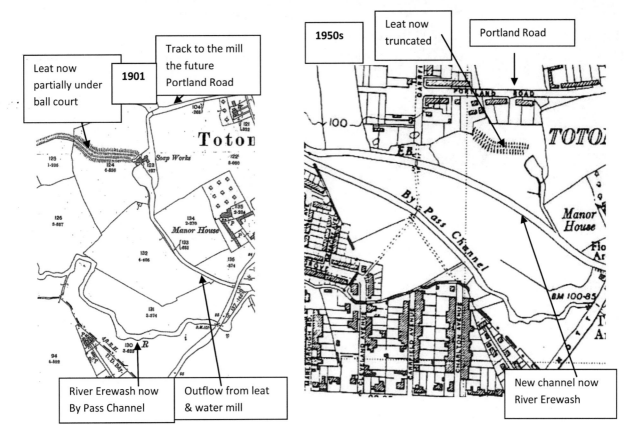

Leat now partially under ball court

1901

Track to the mill the future Portland Road

1950s

Leat now truncated

Portland Road

River Erewash now By Pass Channel

Outflow from leat & water mill

New channel now River Erewash

Following the demise of the mill, the growth of residential buildings and a severe flood in 1932, a new canalised channel was dug and reinforced with concrete "sandbags". This had the effect of creating a "straight" section of river and the By Pass channel, which is more natural and is subject to scouring, erosion and deposition which create different habitats. These two channels vary enormously in character and therefore attract different plants and animals. The old channel, called the By Pass Channel, has more fish species found here than in the main river as this channel has areas of deeper water – pools.

The present River Erewash is a shallow, fast flowing stretch of water. In summer water crowfoot flowers profusely, when the water level

is appropriate (shallow enough). This channel is suitable for salmonidae species of fish with a constant shallow flow and riffles.

River Erewash, shallow in June

Kingfishers and egrets have been recorded along with the larger swans. Insects, butterflies, moths, dragonflies and other invertebrates inhabit the water and the watery margins. Small mammals enjoy these areas and also in other parts of the reserve. The water bat can be seen on summer evenings.

The watery margins and floodplain provide good growing conditions for osiers/willows. Osiers were an important resource to the community. Osier or withy beds and willow holts were the places where the willows/osiers were "farmed". Osier beds at Toton Sidings were rented out in the 19th century.

Willows

Reeds and willows have been used over the centuries in houses. Thatched rooves were made with local products. Willows have also been used in various ways which include basket making, furniture making and the construction of hurdles or movable

March 8th 1882

BY MR. A. E. PALMER.

TOTON SIDINGS, NEAR LONG EATON.

A. E. PALMER, instructed by the MIDLAND RAIL-
WAY COMPANY, will SELL by AUCTION, at the Osier Beds adjoining Toton Sidings, on WED-NESDAY, March 15, about 40 to 50 Tons of Two-year-old OSIERS, Kacksess, Green, Long Skins, Black Mauls.

About 200 Bundles in each Lot.
Sale at Two o'clock.
Auction Offices, Mansfield and Belper.

fences. During the First World War cradles/baskets were specifically made to safeguard the shells being moved from the local Shell Filling factory - modern day bubble wrap. Willows, grown in Toton, were harvested annually and sold on.

Habitats

Various habitats have arisen due to location, soil and rock type. These have been identified as six different compartments namely; A Amenity grassland, B Broadleaved and Mixed plantation C Semi improved or

unimproved neutral grassland, D Broadleaved woodland, E Non native shrubs. The last area (area six) lies adjacent to compartment C. This is industrial land reclaimed by nature. Here there are patches of immature trees and grassland. The riverine areas are also distinct and occur in most compartments.

Compartment A Amenity grassland

This is the land adjacent to Manor Farm Recreation ground. It includes the margins of the sports field with its standing tall hybrid poplars, some of which were reduced in order not to interfere with the power lines and are now standing dead wood, another valuable resource for birds and insects. Alongside the River Erewash and By Pass channel there are corridors of rough grassland and areas of mown grass. The rough grass, in these corridors, provides an appropriate margin for small mammals and invertebrates. Native trees here

include native black poplar, crack and white willow. Maintenance in this area takes into account the needs of the sports players and walkers, while trying to improve the margins for wildlife. Litter removal and containment of Himalayan Balsam and other invasive plants, is an ongoing process.

Compartment B Natural grassland and scrub

This area includes the low lying area between the River Erewash and By Pass channel. The land and banks become more open in this area which at one time made an excellent habitat for the water vole, which likes grassy banks. The aim is to manage this area keeping slow moving water which drops silt and other nutrients, useful for water dwelling creatures. Ponds and scrapes have been created in the area nearer to the Greenwood centre and the Sidings, in order

Creation of scrapes in winter 2015

to diversify the environment for wetland plants, amphibians, and aquatic invertebrates such as dragonflies, pond skaters and whirligigs.

Compartment C Mixed woodland plantation and linear walkway including Banks Road Open space

This area includes open grassland at Banks Road Open space. There is access from here to the Nature Reserve where hedges favoured by many types of wildlife have been planted close to footpaths. These are vibrant in the Autumn with berries and in the Spring and Summer with a variety of flowers and insects. Compartment C is a long narrow strip close to the railway sidings. Within this compartment is an area which is a mixed plantation of deciduous trees. These include ash, rowan (mountain ash), oak, field maple, hawthorn and hazel. Some conifers (pines) were planted in this area as a sound barrier. The scrub habitat which is situated at the edge of the plantation beneath the power lines forms a soft edge of the woodland and is valuable especially for

butterflies and other invertebrates.

Compartment D Parkland between Greenwood Centre and Carrfield Avenue

This compartment includes land north of the River Erewash. It is a fairly formal area with some mown grass but it does contain an old hedge line, an area of brambles (full of delicious blackberries in the Autumn), some scrub and rough grass and herbs on top of the river bank.

Compartment E Rough grassland and scrub west of Greenwood Centre incorporating the northern bank of the River Erewash.

Varied habitats can be found here including mature scrub which is dominated by blackthorn. There is also grassland which is infrequently mown which is the strip of grass close to the bank. The river bank itself is fairly steep accessed in parts by many dogs. Flowers such as convolvulus (bindweed) and tall herbs occur here.

All of these areas are managed by Broxtowe Borough Council in consultation with Friends of Toton Fields. Input by volunteers and enthusiasts such as Norman Lewis help to look after this valuable resource. He and others have spent many hours /days walking the site and talking to contractors from power companies, river management agencies and other organisations. Access to all areas is available as there are many entrances for local residents, dog walkers and others. A permissive horse route is popular and a National Cycle route passes by the edge of Manor Farm Recreation Ground. Further information on the management plan 2017 – 2021 can be found on the website of Broxtowe Borough Council.

Area 6 Toton Sidings. This compartment is a designated Local Wildlife Site (LWS), which is not managed by anyone. It comprises a mix of habitats, with steep banks, grassland and currently supports many immature trees. The redundant railways sidings with their residue of granite and

  limestone ballast, provide homes for a great range of flora and fauna. Fast growing birch is colonising the area following the illegal removal of older trees. It is considered the best brownfield site in the county for its diversity of wildlife.

Sketch map showing the Compartments in relation to some of the roads west of Stapleford Lane.

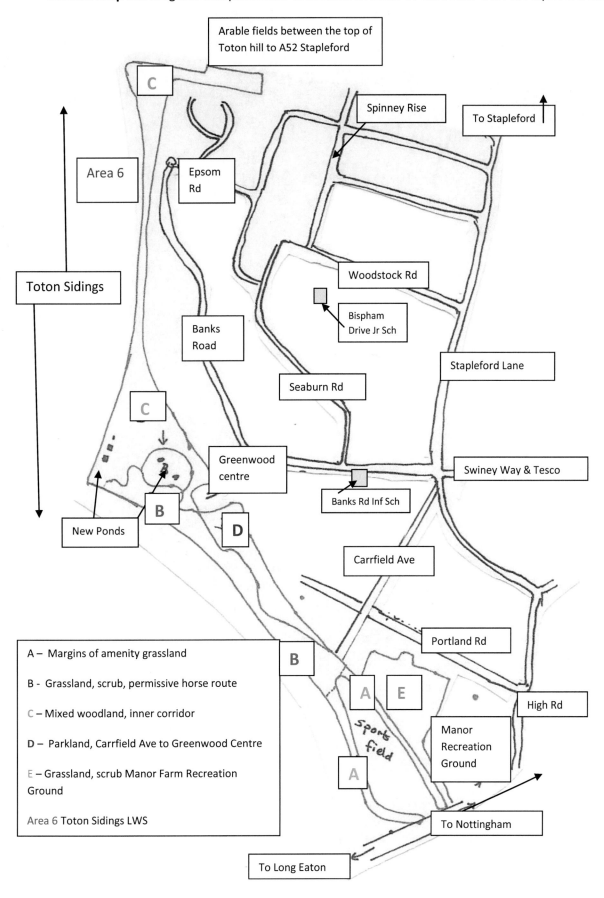

Arable fields between the top of Toton hill to A52 Stapleford

C

Spinney Rise

To Stapleford

Area 6

Epsom Rd

Toton Sidings

Woodstock Rd

Bispham Drive Jr Sch

Banks Road

Stapleford Lane

Seaburn Rd

C

Greenwood centre

Swiney Way & Tesco

New Ponds

B

D

Banks Rd Inf Sch

Carrfield Ave

Portland Rd

A – Margins of amenity grassland

B - Grassland, scrub, permissive horse route

C – Mixed woodland, inner corridor

D – Parkland, Carrfield Ave to Greenwood Centre

E – Grassland, scrub Manor Farm Recreation Ground

Area 6 Toton Sidings LWS

B

A   E

High Rd

Sports field

Manor Recreation Ground

A

To Nottingham

To Long Eaton

11

Toton Fields

Ainslie Carruthers

A Nature Diary

Letters A, B, C, D, E refer to specific areas of Toton, the compartments in previous chapter.

January 1st The New Year dawned with clear blue skies and sunshine throughout the morning with temperatures just above freezing point. The heavy rain during the past evening and melting snow has swelled the River Erewash to high levels. During the afternoon the sky clouded over and rain began to fall as dusk approached.

The first bird for the year was a Blackbird and they are often present well before it is light. As I walk along the riverbank I feel pleasure in hearing Dunnocks singing their songs. They are just short phrases but have spirit and uplift. This song, a fitting start to the New Year as the Dunnock was the bird that started my interest in birding.

When feeding, the Dunnock (hedge sparrow) proceeds in short walks or hops, continually picking up gleanings, minute morsels of food which are very small and disdained by other birds. This recognisable and distinctive walk is totally dissimilar to that of the House Sparrow and was an enigma to me back in the bad winter of 1963. What were these sparrow-like birds superficially like sparrows but so dissimilar in their habits? This puzzle started me off on my interest in ornithology. The Dunnock has been one of my favourite birds ever since.

A flock of Fieldfares feeding on the hawthorn berries at the top of hill look quite resplendent in their grey brown plumage. As they fly they make gentle chacking contact calls. In the *Parlement of Foules* Chaucer introduces them with the phrase 'the frosty feldefares'. Fieldfare means literally the traveller over fields. John Clare includes them in his March poem for the *Shepherd's Calendar:*

...flocking fieldfares, speckled like the thrush,
Picking the red haw from the sweeing bush
That come and go on winters chilling wing
And seem to share no sympathy with the spring.

On the ploughed field 150 Pied Wagtails are feeding, I have not seen this many before. They are all well spread out across the northern part of the field and occasionally some of them fly up and resettle.

One of the most conspicuous features of this bird is their tails, which are constantly dipped up and down, and they have quick and darting movements as they run about searching for food. The poet John Clare caught their movement in the rhyme:

Little trotty wagtail, he went in the rain,
And tittering, tottering sideways he near got straight again
He stooped to get a worm, and look'd up to catch a fly
And then he flew away ere his feathers they were dry.

Nice to see a Meadow Pipit in C, when I saw it I thought it wasn't one of the common species and when it called 'sip, sip, sip' I knew what it was as it flew down into the grass. Meadow Pipits only seem to be present during the early part of the year.

On the top of one of the pylons in C six Magpies stand proud and gleaming white in the sunshine.

Great Tits are singing and they have a many variations in their calls and songs. They have scores of calls and phrases. Its commonest forms are a seesawing, double-noted 'tee-cher', 'tee-cher', and a repeated cry of 'pee-too', 'pee-too', 'pee-too'. Most of the notes are metallic and sound rather like a tiny hammer striking a tiny anvil. Quite often the Great Tit will give a perfect imitation of the 'pink pink' of the chaffinch.

The word Tit is an abbreviation of Titmouse, the family name of this species. Titmouse had nothing to do with mice in its original meaning. The 'mouse' comes from the Old English *mase,* a word used generally for a small bird. Tit came into Middle English from the Icelandic *tittr,* which means small bird. However, in the sixteenth century, the original meaning had been forgotten and *mase,* which by this time had become *mose,* was altered to mouse.

January 5th A Kestrel hovers over C as I walk up and later I see another or the same bird over the Park. The bird hangs in the air, apparently stationary, while it searches the ground beneath. In fact, the bird is not motionless in relation to the air around it. It is facing into the wind so that it gets enough uplift to remain airborne. It spreads its broad tail to supplement the air-catching effect of its spread wings. It also raises its alulas[1], which further reduce the danger of stalling because of turbulence. It separates the feathers at the broad ends of its wings so that little upward jets of air are generated which dispel any turbulent eddies on its upper surfaces. Carefully adjusting these controls, it manages to match exactly its forward motion through the air with the speed of the wind and hangs directly above the patch of ground that it is scanning for prey.

Some species are able to see over a wider colour spectrum than we can. We have three different kinds of cones in our retinas and we detect different shades by combining all three in rather the same way that printers reproduce different tints by using different inks in varying proportions. Birds, on the other hand, have five or six different kinds of cone and some, certainly, can perceive ultra violet light. The Kestrel is one and it has recently been discovered how this might have value for the bird. Voles are one of its main prey. The voles run along regular tracks, collecting their meals, and mark these tracks with little squirts of urine. This helps them find their way and conveys messages of ownership and sexual availability. But it also reveals their paths to a Kestrel, for urine reflects ultra-violet light. So the bird hovering above, knows just where it should look to spot a give-away movement.

---

[1] Alulas = feathers freely moving first digit, a bird's "thumb", and typically bears three to five small flight feathers, with the exact number depending on the species. There also are minor covert feathers overlying the flight feathers.

William Ernest Henley in his poem '*The Windhover*' elegantly describe the hovering of the Kestrel as:

I caught this mornin morning's minion, kingdom of daylight's dauphin, dapple-dawn-drawn falcon, in his riding
Of the rolling level underneath him steady air, and striding
High there, how he rung upon the rein of a wimpling wing
In his ecstasy! Then off, off forth on a swing,
As a skate's heel sweeps smooth on a bow-bend: the hurl and gliding
Rebuffed the big wind. My heart in hiding
Stirred for a bird, - the achieve of, the mastery of the thing!

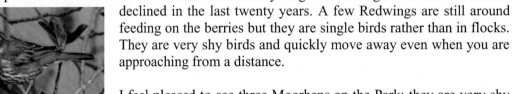

The name, Kestrel, comes from the Old French *crecele,* the modern version of which, *crecerelle* means a rattle. This possibly imitative of the birds' clear 'kee-kee-kee' cry.

Saw three Song Thrushes this morning. It is strange that I see more in the winter than in the summer. In some areas the number of breeding attempts each year is now too few to sustain the population. Overall it seems that the survival of young birds through their first winter has

declined in the last twenty years. A few Redwings are still around feeding on the berries but they are single birds rather than in flocks. They are very shy birds and quickly move away even when you are approaching from a distance.

I feel pleased to see three Moorhens on the Park; they are very shy birds constantly running for cover every time someone approaches. I have never seen a Moorhen on a moor and this is not surprising, as it is not a moorland bird. The 'moor' comes from the Anglo-Saxon word *mor* meaning mere or bog. The Moorhen's toes are particularly long, spreading its weight so that it can walk on floating water plants. There is no webbing between the toes, and perhaps because of this, the Moorhen's swimming action seems laboured, the head jerking forward with each stroke like a cyclist toiling uphill.

First Daisies this morning, in E, they seem reluctant to open. The Daisy, as Chaucer wrote in the best tribute to the daisy, the day's-eye, which opens with the dawn and reflects the sunrise in the pinkish flush on the underside of its petals:

> *Now have I thanne thee eek this condicioun,*
> *That, of al the floures in the mede,*
> *Thanne love I most thise floures white and rede,*
> *Swiche as men callen dayses in our toun.*
> *To hem have I so gret affeccioun,*
> *As I seyde erst, whanne comen is the May,*
> *That in my bed ther daweth me no day*
> *Than I nam up and walkying in the mede*
> *To seen this flour ayein the sonne sprede ...*
> *And lenynge on myne elbow and my syde,*
> *The longe day I shoop me for t'abide*
> *For nothing elles, and I shal not lye,*
> *But for to loke upon the dayesie,*
> *That wel by reson men hit calle may*
> *The 'dayesye' or elles the 'ye of day,'*
> *The emperice and flour of floures alle.*
> *I pray to God that faire mote she falle,*
> *And alle that loven floures, for hire sake!*

There is a saying that spring has not arrived until you can cover three, nine, or a dozen daisy flowers, with your foot. If there is some disagreement about the requisite number, it is because there is scarcely a day in the year when there is not a daisy in flower somewhere.

January 9th A frosty morning with slightly hazy skies and as I walk along the riverbank I see the brilliant white rump of the Green Sandpiper and the dark colour of its wings tinged with olive green. As it searches for food along the water margins it continually bobs up-and-down.

In the Alder copse in C there is a lovely 'charm' of Goldfinches feeding acrobatically on the Alder cones. As they fly they make light tinkling sounds, as delicate as Chinese bells, and this same 'conversational' twittering goes on as they feed together. The collective name for Goldfinches is referred to as a charm. The word 'charm' is defined as 'a blended sound of many voices'; as of birds, schoolchildren, etc. The modern meaning of 'charming' comes from the same roots; the Middle English *charme* and the Latin *carmen* meaning a magic song or spell. Robert Burns rejoiced in: 'The gowdspink, music's gayest child'.

January 12th Walking back along the east side of the By-pass Channel I saw a Grey Wagtail bobbing about in front of me as I walk along. The Grey Wagtail is very much a bird of upland streams and it is very pleasing that it should grace our lowly lowland water in winter.

January 15th A cold and dull morning with a north-easterly wind, but nice to see both the Grey Wagtail and the Green Sandpiper on the By-pass Channel. Ivy berries are in big clusters in E There is a medieval poem about Ivy berries:

> *Ivy bereth beris*
> *As blak as any slow*
> *There commeth the woods colver (pigeon),*
> *And fedeth her of tho;*
> *She lifteth up her taill*
> *And she cakkes or she go;*
> *She would not for a hundred pound*
> *Serve Holly so.*
>
> *Holly with his mery men*
> *They can daunce in hall;*
> *Ivy and her genteel woman*
> *Can not daunce at all,*
> *But like a meine of bullokes*
> *In a water fall,*
> *Or on a hot somers day*
> *Whan they be mad all.*

There are signs of spring vegetation appearing with nettle and cow parsley leaves showing well. A few dandelions are in flower in C. The Dandelion *Taraxacum species,* the name comes from the *dent de lion* – lion's tooth, has more than two hundred microspecies recognised in Britain. The dandelion is well known as an herbal diuretic and laxative and the leaves and flowers can be added to salads. They are often gathered for making wine, the classic account of which is in Laurie Lee's *Cider with Rosie.* A substantial amount of molehills in C the moles have been quite busy in the last day or two.

January 16th A very frosty and misty morning. Not so many birds about but I feel amply rewarded as I see a flash of blue on the By-pass Channel, a Kingfisher, it flies swiftly downstream, then a few moments later it dives into the water and emerge with a fish. I am very pleased about this because I was very worried that last November's floods might have carried the small fish away.

Frederick William Faber, in a poem about the River Cherwell, writes of the sharp streak of colour, which marks the shy kingfisher's straight, and undeviating flight:

There came
Swift as a meteor's shining flame
A kingfisher from out of the brake
And almost seemed to leave a wake
Of brilliant hues behind

As I was watch the Kingfisher, the Green Sandpiper is bobbing about in the same area. Two attractive birds at the same time. Earlier I saw a fox in this area. I often see them here and we nearly bumped into each other at times. Foxes have been leaving their calling cards around a lot of the areas just lately.

January 22nd After a cool damp start it has turned warmer. I see a flock of about 40 Greenfinches in C and a substantial numbers of molehills at the end of C. A similar amount was in E near the tennis courts. The sound of the (tchack) call of the Jackdaw is very reminiscent of the Peak District and it is very pleasing to hear them.

February 7th Bright sunny, but cool, morning. I watch a Sparrowhawk soaring over C being mobbed by a Carrion Crow. The hawk is far too agile for the crow who gives up and flies away.

Watched two Robins in territorial threat display in C. Each pushes their chests forward in a threatening manner, neither making an audible sound. This continues for some time and they are joined by a third Robin who joins in the display. All three posture together before eventually separating.

See six Stock Doves on the arable field at the top of the hill beyond the reserve. I do not see this species very often. The Skylark in the same area is now in full song but I cannot actually see it. The skylark has inspired many fine lines of poetry, and perhaps the most famous being, *Ode to a Skylark,* by Shelley:

Hail to thee, blithe spirit!
thou never wert,
That from heaven, or near it,
Pourest thy full heart
In profuse strains of unpremeditated art.

Higher still and higher
From the earth thou springest
Like a cloud of fire;
The blue deep thou wingest,
And singing still does soar, and soarest ever singing

Wordsworth also has many a fine line:

A privacy of glorious light is thine:
Whence thou does pour upon the world a flood
Of harmony, with instinct more divine

February 13th Bright sunny morning after overnight frost. Heard six Song Thrushes singing this morning, two in D, one thrush singing a lot louder than the other. Highest Dunnock count of the year, 23, with most of them singing.

Numerous Pied Wagtails (61) are on the ploughed field, they continually flit about from one spot to another, like white leaves in the wind.

Not much song so far this year from the Mistle Thrushes, although they there are often seen feeding in the middle of the park. The few Blackbirds that venture onto the park only feed at the edges.

The Mistle Thrush (Turdus viscivorus). *Visvcivoros,* the second part of the scientific name coined by Linnaeus, is basically the same as its standard English name *viscum* = mistletoe and *voro* = devour. The Mistle Thrush and its fondness for berries was mentioned by Aristotle in his *History of Animals* written in the fourth century BC. Mistletoe berries are an important food for the bird in Mediterranean countries where a species of mistletoe with red berries grows abundantly on olive trees, but in the British Isles it has not been proved that mistletoe is part of its diet at all. But the name, derived from Aristotle's early description has been carried through to the standard name of the present day.

The name thrush, or rather the Anglo-Saxon *thysce,* has been in use for over a thousand years and the Mistle Thrush and Song Thrush have been distinguished as separate species since the eighth century. The French have a word *'grievel',* from *Grieve,* a thrush, which means speckled like a thrush.

First Yellowhammer song this morning, the bird is singing from the top of a hawthorn bush in C 'A-little-bit-of-bread-but-no-cheese' as the song is often described.

Nice to hear a Willow Tit in C, I seldom see it but its call is distinctive. It was only distinguished from the Marsh Tit in 1897, and was the last native British breeding species to achieve recognition. The discovery was not found by ornithologists in the field but by systematists going through a tray of specimens marked 'Marsh Tit', in the British Museum, and noticed two birds which were decidedly a different species. Over the years I only see one or two Willow Tits in Toton and it is long time since I saw one in the garden. The CBC index[2] bird shows a 50% decline over 1972 to 1996 and 30% over the five years 1994-98 in the Breeding Birds Survey. This is a serious decline.

Another bird declining in Toton is the House Sparrow; there has been a significant lessening in numbers. One theory put forward to explain the decline is a possible lack of insect food during the vital days when the nestlings need extra protein. The CBC index reports a decline of 64% over 25 years.

February 16th A bright sunny morning and no overnight frost, but quite cool. First Chaffinch song this morning. The song consists of a few piping little introductory notes, followed by a twittery trill ending in a short flourish. In his poem 'The Lover and the Birds' William Allingham interprets this as:

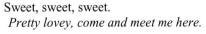

Sweet, sweet, sweet.
Pretty lovey, come and meet me here.

The Scots poet, Grahame describes Chaffinches as:
When not a strain is head through all the woods,
I've seen the shilfa light from off his perch
And hop into a shallow of the stream,
Then, half-afraid, flit to shore, then i
Again alight and dip his rosy breast,
And fluttering wings, while dew-like globules coursed
The plumage of his brown empurpled back.

---

[2] CBC Common Bird census compiled by British Trust for ornithology

Collared Doves are regular visitors to the area. This dove can be regarded as the success story of the 20th Century. Since they first started to breed in Norfolk in 1955 they have increased in numbers quite dramatically. By 1970 there may have been as many as 25,000 pairs in Britain Ireland and the CBC index increased fivefold between 1972 and 1996. The Collared Dove monotonous tri-syllabic call, a mournful 'coo-coo-ook' has not yet been translated into a vernacular name.

February 20th A dull slightly damp morning, but a bit warmer. Saw two Black-headed Gulls in full breeding plumage. Their head is not really black, it is chocolate-brown. They are a quite a noisy gull first thing in the morning when they come down onto the park to feed, although their call is not so evocative of the sea as the Herring Gull.

The Kestrel is in usual place perched on the tennis courts wire post and a Yellowhammer is in C again. The Green Sandpiper turned up again this morning now that the river is at a lower level. The highest count of Dunnocks with 23 singing males and highest count of Magpies so far this year, a total of sixty, with 29 seen in D. Seeing so many Magpies reminds me of the old rhyme in regard to the number seen on a walk:

> *One's sorrow, two's mirth,*
> *Three's a wedding, four's a birth,*
> *Five's a christening, six a dearth,*
> *Seven's heaven, eight is hell,*
> *And nine's the devil his ane sel'.*

There are, of course, many other similar versions.

February 23rd A sunny morning and not so cold. No overnight frost. The Goat Willow buds are starting to show in E. Although there are a lot of Mistle Thrushes around, ten today nine of them on the park, I haven't heard any song since January 28th. A couple of days ago there was a report in the paper that a Swallow had been seen at Slapton Ley in Devon. The Greek proverb, 'One swallow does not make spring', is to be found in Aristotle's *Nicomachoean Ethics (I, vii, 16)*. The full proverb states:

The Good of man is the active exercise of or virtue. Moreover this activity must occupy a complete lifetime; for one swallow does not make spring, nor does one fine day; and similarly one day or a brief period of happiness does not make a man supremely blessed or happy.

First Blackbird song this morning. I think that the song of the Blackbird surpasses the song of any other bird, including that of the Nightingale and Skylark. Both the latter have excellent songs and Keat's description of the Nightingale's song as '*singeth of summer with full-throated ease*' could equally apply to that of the blackbird. I find his song beautiful and melodic with tuneful harmonic phrases.

February 24th A bright cloudless sunny morning no wind but very cool after overnight frost. There are two Grey Wagtails in D flitting along together in front of me as I walk along the By Pass Channel.

A Hawthorn bush is practically in full leaf in E. The Hawthorn is the commonest tree in Toton Fields and apart from being common in the remaining hedgerows it also appears in significant numbers away from the hedgerows. Some of these plants are of a scrubby nature but in parts they have grown into quite tall trees. It is quite a resilient plant and reluctant to give way to other types of woodland species.

In Ireland lone Hawthorns belong to the fairies and cannot be disturbed and this is described in William Allingham's poem –

Up the airy mountain, down the rushy glen'
the craggy hillside
the mosses bare,
They have planted thorn trees
For pleasure here and there,
Is any man so daring
As dig them up in spite,
He shall find their sharpest thorns
In his bed at night.

The Hawthorn was chosen Henry VII, as his device, because Richard III's crown was recovered from a hawthorn bush at Bosworth.

February 27th A dull wet morning with sleety rain and in the afternoon a heavy shower of hail. In parts of Scotland and Northern England there have been heavy falls of snow and roads have been blocked. The river is high this morning and the Kingfisher was feeding in the small dyke that runs into the Overflow channel, which is shallower.

There are two Skylarks this morning and this is the first time for years that I have seen two together in Toton. Again I see two separate sightings of Kestrels, both females, one on the Park and one in C. Quite a long way apart giving rise to my supposition that there are two separate birds.

Elder is also in leaf this morning. The Elder is another tree with a wealth of superstition about it. In various countries there are records of an elder spirit or an elder mother who is her own tree and

protects it at the same time, and traces of the Elder's old power are not yet erased from the English or Irish mind. Elder must not be burnt. If you put it on the fire, you will see the devil sitting on the chimney pot. In Derbyshire it is called the 'Devil's Wood'.

The Green Woodpecker has been both seen and heard on four occasions and a female Great Spotted Woodpecker put in an appearance on the 5th. A Skylark has been singing above the arable fields throughout the month and a second bird was also seen on the 27th. On three occasions there were large numbers of Pied Wagtails feeding on the arable fields and a Grey Wagtail graced the overflow channel on four occasions together with a second one on the 24th.

The number of Wrens seen has fluctuated but on the 19th I saw eleven which was very encouraging. Before this month I was getting very concerned about the poor numbers of sightings of Dunnocks, however sightings have increased and on two occasions there were 30 birds and on one day there was 23 singing males.

Robin numbers have dwindled slightly during the month and Blackbird numbers have varied from day-to-day peaking in the seventies on two occasions. The only time I heard a Blackbird singing was on the 23rd. Only once did I see Fieldfares but Redwings were seen on every day I went out.

Up to twelve Mistle Thrushes are present with most of them seen in the park area, but a significant lack of song. There are least eight Song Thrushes; seven of them singing males, which is a very good sign that the species may be recovering, in Toton at least.

Two wintering Blackcaps were seen just outside of my garden on the 24th and one day I saw a possible Chiffchaff in C but it was disturbed before I could make a positive identification. The Willow Tit was only seen on one occasion, but small numbers of Long-tailed Tits have been present and good numbers of Blue and Great Tits. Magpie numbers fluctuate from day-to-day but on two occasions over sixty birds were present.

House Sparrow numbers continued to dwindle with only two days when numbers topped fifty. Chaffinches have been regular in small numbers and their first song on the 16th. Good numbers of Greenfinches have been present in small flocks. It was pleasing to see Bullfinches towards the end of the month and the presence of up to four Yellowhammers throughout the whole period with two singing males.

It has been a good bird month for Toton with a total of 45 species and some very pleasing sightings. However all the birds and their behaviour are always interesting whether they are rare or common.

March 3rd Cold frosty morning partly cloudy. In D a Moorhen is sidling across the river towards another on the side of the bank. The one sidling across the river suddenly leaps at the other and a lot of squawking takes place and a chase up river with head down and flapping wings. It is obviously territorial behaviour.

There is something magical and exhilarating about the sound of the water as it flows over the pebbles and weirs. I never tire of hearing it each time I go out.

A Reed Bunting seen in C is the first seen since 19th January. Years ago they used to be seen in the garden on a regular basis, but now I only see one or two in the D areas. The CBC index for the period between 1972 and 1996 records a 64% loss.

Heard a Green Woodpecker calling in the gardens at the end of E

March 4th First Gorse in flower this year, other years I have seen it in flower in January. The Gorse *Ulex europaeus,* wherever grown in quantity, is one of the great landscape plants showing a blaze of yellow. Swedish naturalist Linneaus reputedly fell to his knees and thanked God when he first saw it on an English common. It is one of the most sensual of plants – the flowers smelling of coconut and vanilla, and the seed pods crack in the hot sunshine.

March 5th A male Sparrowhawk is being mobbed by Carrion Crows as it flies over the park. In E a pink underside of a Daisy catches my eye as I walk along. It makes the whole area seem brighter.

In C a congregation of Crows (12) gather in a hawthorn bush halfway up the hillside. In C there seems to be a strong smell of fox in every part of the wood.

Four Feral Pigeons in D, not a bird that I usually see in Toton, although there are quite a lot at Long Eaton market place. Two Goldfinches in C, are a welcome touch of colour.

March 6th Bright sunny morning after overnight frost. Two Magpies are at the nest site at the main road end of E. Like yesterday, it seems to be the gathering of the Crows time. There are seven on a poplar tree on the park.

About 30 Lapwings fly over the park heading towards Attenborough. The origin of the name Lapwing comes from the Anglo-Saxon word *hleapewince* – literally 'run' and 'wink'. This describes the flight of the Lapwing as it rises from the ground on slowly beating wings as it steadily climbs, then goes into a twisting, rolling dive which ends with an upward twist and a flurry of rapid, buzzing wing-beats. The haunting cry of 'pee-wit' evokes nostalgia for the wildness of upland nature and the remoteness from human habitation.

Forty-four Greenfinches this morning distributed about the area and two Kingfishers, one at each end of the By-pass Channel. First Reed Bunting song of the year in C. The song is rather brief and simple.

March 9th First Coltsfoot of the year at the top of the hill. The flowers of Coltsfoot, *Tussilago farfara,* are flowering in E. Their cheerful yellow blooms and scaly stems, appear a month or so before the leaves. The common name originally written'Colt's-foot' describes the hoof-like shape of the leaves, which are mealy above when they first appear and covered with white felt beneath. The Scots call the plant 'tushylucky' which is a corruption of the Latin *tussilago* a name used by Pliny, related to *tussis*, a cough – who records the use of the leaves as a cough medicine. The leaf still has its place as a demulcent[3] against coughs in the *British Pharmaceutical Codex (1949).* Pectoral beers, jelly and wine have also been made from Coltsfoot leaves.

First Linnet song this morning. The name Linnet comes from the Old English *linece,* from the Latin *linum* = the flax family. Flax once grown widely, has declined and the seeds no longer form part of the Linnet's diet. Highest numbers of Dunnocks (36)and Robins (34) so far this year.

March 12th Definitely two Kestrels in Toton because two are flying together in E. First Coal Tit of the year in Toton, this one in E. This is a bird of conifers, hence the very few sightings locally

March 13th Cool sunny morning. A male Blackcap in the end garden next to C in a tree covered in Ivy. Blackcaps are more vegetarian than other warblers in their diet and in early spring they tend to feed on ivy berries and tree flowers. While searching among the vegetation it was uttering a muted sub-song.

A great surprise this morning is a Cock Pheasant that strolls out in front of me from the riverside in D and walks across quite nonchalantly to the bushes on the other side. A very resplendent bird! Only the second time that I have seen one in Toton. If I saw a Pheasant out in the countryside I would feel pleased but not necessary enriched, but when I see an unusual or unexpected species on my own patch this does give me a feeling of enrichment. The feeling that Keat's describes in his poem, 'In First Looking into Chapman's Homer' as:

> *Much have I travell'd in the realms of gold,*
> *And many goodly states and kingdoms seen;*
>
> *Round many western islands have I been*
> *Which bards in fealty to Apollo hold,*
> *Oft of one wide expanse had I been told*
> *That deep-brow'd Homer ruled as his demesne;*
> *Yet did I never breathe its pure serene*
> *Till I heard Chapman speak out loud and bold:*
> *Then felt I like some watcher of the skies*
> *When a new planet swims into his ken;*
> *Or like stout Cortez when with eagle eyes*
> *He stared at the Pacific-and all his men*
> *Look'd at each other with wild surmise-*
> *Silent, upon a peak in Darien.*

---

[3] Demulcent = a substance that relieves irritation of the mucous membranes in the mouth by forming a protective film.

Two Dunnocks are displaying in C and two male Yellowhammers are calling

As I turn into the homeward stretch in E there stands before me a beautiful display of Lesser Celandines, about fifty in full flower, all like brightly shining stars in the sunshine. Local names such as 'Starflower' and 'Spring Messenger' are very apt descriptions.

With few plants flowering at this time of year, Lesser Celandines and Coltsfoot provide a welcome source of pollen and nectar for early bees and butterflies.

Nearby a Goldcrest gently calls and flits by, displaying its gold crown. Later, in E, a Bumble Bee with a yellow rump flies by. Two complementary bright objects on the same walk.

The sound of the river always enchants me as I walk by, especially at the end of C where it comes by in a great bend, and shoals in various places. The sound of the water over the pebbles reminds me of a verse from the 'Nightingale' sung in a Lancashire dialect: *'She loves to hear the watter rattle and the nightingale sing'*. Rattle is a more descriptive of water flowing over pebbles than ripple.

March 14th Just after six as I was getting up I heard the sound of Greylag Geese calling and I quickly went to the window and saw a pair flying overhead, a new bird for Toton. Went out at 7 a.m. this morning, it was lovely and fresh after a slight overnight frost.

Two Goldcrests in C are flitting around a hawthorn bush searching for insects. One of them spreads its crest and reveals its brilliant orange crown. The voice of the Goldcrest is very high pitched; the call notes are like needle points of sound. Lord Grey of Fallodon describes the Goldcrest's song as 'suggesting a tiny stream trickling and rippling over a small pebbly channel, and at the end going over a miniature cascade'.

My patch, the narrowest piece of green belt in Broxtowe, and sandwiched between two urban areas, has a many different habitats. These range from a main river, an overflow channel, wetland, scrub and rough grassland, woodland, old hedgerows, disused railway sidings, playing fields, council maintained grassland, and arable fields.

Over one hundred species of birds have been seen in the area and new species keep turning up. Wild plants, excluding grasses and sedges, exceed two hundred species. To the average person the area would hold little attraction, apart from numerous dog walkers and the occasional jogger. Seldom do I see another person that is not accompanied by a dog, except for a few train spotters at the top of Toton Hill. Yet is has a great many attractions, the area is a microcosm of different habitats that can be found elsewhere in the countryside, and it is possible, as far as birds are concerned, for anything to turn up. But the excitement and satisfaction is not in seeing a rarity or a rare plant, it is in the ability to observe, at close hand, the passage of the seasons as it affects the local flora and fauna. To see the changes, see the unexpected, and to enjoy the commonplace is a joy. As you walk along, you come to expect a particular bird will be in a certain place and come to regard them as friends, missing them if they are not there. As I have said I am very lucky to have such an area on my doorstep and such a wealth of wildlife to accompany my walks.

March 19th Cloudless morning after overnight frost and still quite cool. A massive Gorse bush is in flower on the sidings. This seems to be the only one left in Toton Fields, as previously there were three bushes in the area. I hear the Green Woodpecker calling, the sound *Yaffle* this name and several variations have been in common usage since the end of the eighteenth century. The Old English name for the bird was *Hyghwhele* and this has given rise to such names as Hewhole, High Hoe or Wood Awl. John of Guildford's poem the *Owl and the Nightingale* refers to the Woodpecker as *Wudewale* as does Chaucer in the *Romaunt of the Rose* (1369).

March 20th Another overnight frost followed by a dull cold morning. First Red Dead Nettle of the year flowering in E the first Dandelion clocks. Shakespeare included dandelion clocks in the elegy *Cymbeline:*

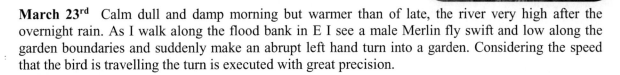

Golden lads and girls all must
As chimney-sweepers come to dust
Keats imagined:
The soft rustle of a maidens gown
Fanning away the dandelion's down

March 23rd Calm dull and damp morning but warmer than of late, the river very high after the overnight rain. As I walk along the flood bank in E I see a male Merlin fly swift and low along the garden boundaries and suddenly make an abrupt left hand turn into a garden. Considering the speed that the bird is travelling the turn is executed with great precision.

In "Mallard Reach" I see two ducks sitting together on a mud bank. One, a Mallard flies off and the other, a Goosander, slowly gets up and quite calmly enters the river and lets the current take him downstream. This makes the second unusual bird to be seen in Toton in one day.

First black slug of the year and many worms stranded on the paths, each one gently returned to a more suitable environment. Nice to see the male Reed Bunting again in C.

Robin songs are getting more vigorous; especially where there are competing males nearby.

March 26th Damp, cloudy and cool morning. Two Moorhens out on the park at the west end, but no recent sightings of any Moorhens at the east end of the park. Another Moorhen is on the field adjacent to B. This is the first time that I have seen one on the other side of the By Pass channel.

Highest House Sparrow total of the year, so far, 74. The flock in C accounts for the increase in numbers, hitherto they have been elsewhere but now they have returned.

March 27th A cold, dull and damp morning. Two Skylarks and eight Fieldfares on the arable fields. Yesterday two Redwings were still present. A surprise bird is a Meadow Pipit seen in C; this is only the second one I have seen this year in Toton. The last one was on New Year's Day. I usually see one each year in January and that's it, this year I have been lucky to see another. This is another bird which is quite common in certain parts of the country but when you see it in your own area it adds excitement to the day. I find the Meadow Pipit a quite attractive bird but the British Museum published a few verses on the subject of pipit taxonomy some years ago, which began:

It's a pity pipits have
No diagnostic features
Specifically they are the least
Distinctive of God's creatures

It is very misty this morning and even the power station can hardly be seen as the cooling towers and chimney are shrouded in mist. Throughout the year the smoke from the power station chimney and the steam from the cooling towers has a detrimental effect on local weather in Toton. Quite often the sun can be obscured for lengthy periods of time.

March 28th Dull, damp, cloudy morning, later turning to heavy rain. I see a Magpie on its nest and a Starling gathering nesting material. Greenfinches have been quite numerous this month and their calls have been a significant feature of my walks.

Three Skylarks over the arable fields this morning, two of them singing. None of the five fields have been planted although two of them have been ploughed.

March 30th Cool damp morning after overnight rain. First yellow banded snail and first Chiffchaffs of the year in E. Lord Grey of Fallodon said that - "the Chiffchaff, alone of all the warblers has given us the right to expect him in March; he is the forerunner of the rush of song-birds that is on its way to us and will arrive in April, and thereafter enrich our woods, meadows and gardens with still further variety and quality of song. This is why the first hearing of a Chiffchaff moves us so each spring. He is a symbol, a promise, an assurance of what is to come."

Lord Grey goes on to say – "While the Chiffchaff is classed as a warbler there is, however, no conceivable utmost stretch of definition by which the term 'warble' can be applicable to the sound that the Chiffchaff makes. By the season and manner of utterance the Chiffchaff gives us clearly to understand that he intends his notes to be a song. Ill-disposed persons may say that it is nothing more than chirping: against this assertion I protest. There is spirit in the two notes that suggests the same motive as song, and there is something more than the mere reiteration of two notes. To one who listens attentively there is a hint of a pattern in the variation of the notes. The sounds suggests industry, as of the passage of a shuttle to and fro."

March 31st Dull, cloudy morning. The first Swallow of the year is flying low over the cricket pitch and in E . A female Chaffinch is gathering nest material. A Blackbird is collecting nesting material in C. A Goldcrest is also present in C.

Quite a lot of Coltsfoot at the top of Toton Hill. A rewarding sight was one of a Sweet Violet, the flower of Aphrodite, the goddess of love.

Black-headed Gull numbers have been few, with only two days where numbers reached double figures. Collared Doves have already bred in area C. The Kingfisher has been present on the By Pass Channel adjacent to the Manor Park and a second one further upstream

April 2nd Bright sunny morning and quite a lot warmer. The path through E is lovely as it is transformed on both sides by willow catkins of various varieties. A Small Tortoiseshell butterfly in E and two Linnets in their normal breeding territory, near the bowling green.

First Willow Warbler of the year, in E. The Willow Warblers song is one of the most common sounds of the countryside. Lord Grey of Fallodon found the arrival and first hearing of the Willow Warbler each spring as a moving incident. He described the song "as a succession of slender and delicate notes, forming a completed sentence, which is repeated again and again at short intervals. The notes have a very endearing quality of their own. They suggest something plaintive – as if the bird were pleading - a cadence of soft summer rain."

Coward quotes one of the best verbal descriptions of its song. *"A tender delicious warble with a dying fall... It mounts up round and full, then runs down the scale, and expires upon the air in a gentle murmur"*. In Witherby's "Sound Guide to British Birds" it is represented as 'seep-seep tye-tye-tye-tway-tway weriwi weer.

Two Blackcaps are singing in E. The poet John Clare wrote a poem about the Blackcap called the 'March Nightingale'. Lord Grey of Fallodon wrote *"For perfection or moving quality of voice I should place the blackcap with the blackbird and nightingale in the first class of British song-birds. His song is loud, exceedingly sweet, but also spirited: it is not very long, but is frequently repeated: there is not great variety, but the thing done is absolutely perfect. There is not a note that fails to please or to be a success."*

I saw a Peacock butterfly in E. A Greenfinch is gathering nesting material in D They nest in forked branches or against a tree trunk, sometimes in a thick bush. The nest is a large cup of twigs, moss, lichen and grass, lined with softer materials like hair.

At present most Blackbirds are singing at dawn or dusk, but two, one in D and one in C are singing throughout the morning. There is a high number of Dunnocks again – 34, including 26 singing males, equalling the best total this year and also recorded the second highest total of Robins – 29 this year.

Two Mute Swans fly over toward the north-west as I walk through C and later I saw a pair in the By-pass Channel in E. The Green Woodpecker has been seen and heard over quite an area but rarely seen in the same place twice.

Six Song Thrushes have been observed singing and up to nine have been observed although song has been infrequent. Magpie numbers averaged about thirty birds with several seen at the nest. Two male Yellowhammers have been observed singing with up to five birds present. The most noticeable recently for its calls and song has been the Greenfinch.

April 3rd A bright start but quickly turning cloudy and cool. Three Chiffchaffs singing this morning in E.

April 7th Still three singing Chiffchaff's present. Two Willow Warblers today in D.

April 13th Sunny morning with Blackthorn in blossom. The Blackthorn is becoming the dominant shrub in E. When I first came to Toton in 1963 the hedgerows were quite small in width. Now, because of its rampant habit of spreading sideways, it has created dense thickets.

Yellowhammer in C again they seem to be extending down the hill which is a very good sign. Two Bullfinches in D.

April 16th Dull morning with very little wind and slightly damp. A fully flowered Cow Parsley on the park. Breeding has now starting in earnest. I observe a discarded small pale blue egg in E; a Blackbird gathering nesting material in E; and a Long Tailed Tit gathering nesting material in C.

Only just realised that you can see Breedon-on-the Hill Church from the top of Toton Hill. Indeed you can see

over three counties and quite often watch planes fly over and follow their progress as they circle round and land at East Midlands Airport.

April 17th Cold cloudy morning after overnight frost. Nice to see two Song Thrushes in C and a Willow Tit in D. Willow Tit sightings are getting fewer in the fields and none at all in the garden. A solitary male Mallard is sitting on the bank in Mallard Reach, he has been by himself for a few days now. A Water Vole is seen swimming across the river in D, I do not see them very often but there are several holes in the riverbanks.

In the bushes at the west end of D, a Magpie is being hassled by two Blue Tits, two Long Tailed Tits and a Blackbird with a great deal of noise and hectic movement.

April 20th On the Park near the south east end a Magpie is trying to hassle a recently fledged Mistle Thrush. An adult Mistle Thrush keeps swooping on the Magpie with quite acrobatic dives, turns and near hits and succeeds in driving the Magpie away. Nearby a Mistle Thrush is carrying food in E. Two Mistle Thrushes in E are hassling a Carrion Crow in the tall tree near the tennis courts.

April 24th Dull morning with little wind. A Blackbird is gathering nesting material in E. A pair of Mallard in the wet area of B, this is the first time that I have seen mallard there. Magpie numbers have now reached their lowest – 9, the flocks have dispersed and the paired females are obviously sitting on nests.

April 25th A dull and damp morning, later turning to mixed showers and sunshine. A Moorhen at the west end of the park, I wonder if the other one is nesting somewhere or just disappeared? Fresh molehills in D and first Bluebells in flower in D. Robert Burns, rejecting the gaudier flowers of foreign fields, describes the Bluebell as:

> *For dearer to me are you bumble broom bowers*
> *Where the bluebell and the gowan lurk lowly unseen:*
> *For there, lightly tripping amongst the wild flowers,*
> *A-listening the linnet, aft wanders my Jean.*

Bluebell, as a name, only came into common currency early in the nineteenth century when the Romantic poets began to celebrate it.

In C a Starling is carrying food probably to a female on the nest. A pair of Yellowhammers in C. Three Song Thrushes and three Mistle Thrushes are singing today.

Dandelions quite prolific both at the top hedgerow bank in C and along the north bank of the By Pass Channel. The poet Howard Nemerov wrote dandelions referring to them as common suns, nearly as common as grass which start green and then shine before changing to a ghost within week.

April 27th Bright sunny morning. White Dead Nettle, a Goldfinch singing in E. A Peacock butterfly in E and a Small Tortoiseshell Butterfly. Three Moorhens in D, and the first Common Whitethroat at the top of Toton Hill. Flitting from bush to bush with bursts of song.
John Clare describes the Whitethroat in his poem 'The Happy Bird':

> *The happy Whitethroat on the sweeing bough,*
> *Swayed by the impulse of the gadding wind*
> *That ushers in the showers of April, now*
> *Carols right joyously; and now reclined,*
> *Crouching, she clings close to her moving seat,*
> *To keep her hold; and till the wind for rest*
> *Pauses, she mutters inward melodies,*
> *That seem her heart's rich thinkings to repeat,*

But when the branch is still, her little breast
Swells out in rapture's gushing symphonies;
And then, against her brown wing softly prest,
This way and that she swees – till gusts arise
More boisterous in their play, then off she flies.

The Whitethroat suffered a massive mortality in 1969 attributed to a drought in the Sahel[4]. The CBC index dropped 75% and there was a further 50% decline over the next five years. Gradual recovery was reversed in 1984-85 because of the same reason, but subsequently prospects have been quite good. The five-year BBS[5] figures show a 14% increase.

In C a Magpie has got a Starling down on the ground and is pecking away at it. It eventually got away and the Magpie is then harried by a whole flock of Starlings.

April Summary We seem to have lost one of the pairs of Moorhens on the park, only those at the west end have been seen and normally only one intermittently. The Kestrel has only been seen twice and the Kingfisher only once. However as the river has been high throughout most of the month the lack of Kingfisher sightings is not surprising.

The Skylark has been singing throughout the month but the Green Woodpecker heard only once. Dunnock totals peaked at 34 then averaged about 19. Robin totals have been constant around the 20 mark and Blackbirds averaging around 40 with a peak of 60 on the 14th.

Song Thrush numbers have dropped, but six were present on the 16th. The first Common Whitethroat was seen and heard on the 27th. Two/three Chiffchaffs have been present throughout the month and Willow Warblers have built up their numbers to 14.

Long-tailed Tits have no longer been seen in foraging flocks and only a pair has been seen on a regular basis. Blue and Great Tit numbers have been constant but only one sighting of a Willow Tit.

Magpie sightings have gradually reduced as breeding commenced and House Sparrow numbers have gradually risen reaching 86 on the 27th. Up to three pairs of Yellowhammers are present and one singing male Reed Bunting.

May 2nd Clear sunny morning. First Hawthorn blossom out in E, and a Rabbit in C' Several Peacock and Small Tortoiseshell Butterflies about this morning.

One Lady's-smock is flowering on the By-pass Channel bank in D. Last year there were several plants flowering until they were cut down by the mowing regime of Severn Trent. I prefer the name Lady's-Smock to the plants 'approved' English name – Cuckooflower. This spring flower is associated with milkmaids and their smocks and the Cuckoo. Gerard, the first English botanist to record the flower wrote, *Cardamine pratensis* comes out 'for the most part of April and May, when the Cuckoo begins to sing her pleasant note without stammering'. It is interesting to note that many early poets and writers often associated bird song with the female of the species.

Shakespeare wrote 'lady-smocks all silver white' in the song from Love's Labour Lost and an Irish poet wrote in the fifteenth/sixteenth century
Tender cress and cuckoo flower:
And curly-haired, fair headed maids,
Sweet was the sound of their singing.

---

[4] Sahel- an area south of the Sahara, north of the African grasslands, west and central Africa.
[5] Breeding bird survey British Trust for Ornithology

Both poets and botanists have called the flower white when it is more of a pale lilac colour.

May 7ᵗʰ Fine sunny morning after almost a week without any rain! Welcome sight of the Kingfisher in the By-pass Channel, as it swiftly flies upstream and perches on an overhanging branch. The Kingfishers suffer from lack of perching places on the By Pass Channel as the water authority have a severe bank management regime and only in E are there any suitable perching places and these are very few.

White Dead Nettle, Honesty and Jack-by-the-Hedge flowering, The aroma of the May Blossom is quite pervasive. At the west end of C is a large Crab Apple, the buds are not yet open but they are showing a lovely shade of deep pink. The top slopes in C are so covered in daisies and dandelions that the grass can hardly be seen. It is like looking at a magic carpet.

Saw several Tortoiseshell, Peacocks and White butterflies this morning. Four Song Thrushes singing plus two more none vocalists. Saw first Swifts this morning, three flying fast overhead. Whitethroat numbers are rising, but Willow Warbler numbers have slightly dropped.

May 8ᵗʰ Bright sunny warm morning. The trees in various stage of leaf are showing a varied hue of lovely colours. In the By Pass Channel there are a Goldfinch and a male House Sparrow bathing side by side in the shallow water. The Sparrow looks very drab beside the Goldfinch and the yellow on the Goldfinch outshines the nearby dandelions. A Chaffinch and a Greenfinch join the bathing party until the Chaffinch decides to chase the Goldfinch away.

First House Martin of the year, one flies low over the park. A Spotted Flycatcher perches on a branch in D. A first for me in Toton. A Heron is being mobbed by two Carrion Crows in D.

First Speckled Wood Butterfly in C. A passing Fox has a very big bushy tail. A Reed Bunting is singing in the marshy area of D.

May 9ᵗʰ A flock of about 100 Wood Pigeons on the arable fields today and the highest total yet of Yellowhammers – eight!

May 15ᵗʰ The river is very high after heavy overnight rain. In the dyke I see a Mallard with ten very young ducklings. I think that she is very sensible keeping the ducklings in relatively calm water, but later, however, I see all of them being swiftly carried down the By Pass Channel.

May 18ᵗʰ About 300 Starlings today, with a large proportion being newly fledged young.

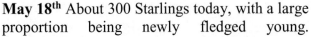

Everywhere there seems to be young starlings begging food with loud cries. Cow Parsley is now fully out but the May Blossom is only to be seen on very few bushes. Meadow Buttercups are showing very vigorous growth with many flowering on very long stems.

Cow Parsley has been described as 'Queen Anne's Lace' so called because when Queen Anne travelled the countryside in May the people said that the roadsides had been decorated for her. The story is that Queen Anne, who suffered from asthma, used to come out into the countryside around Kensington, then over meadow and farmland, to get fresher air. As she and her ladies walked along the country lanes in spring sunshine, they carried their lace pillows and made lace. The flowering cow parsley, with its beautiful, lacy flowers, resembled the court ladies' lace patterns, and so country folk began to call it Queen Anne's Lace, a name which persists today.
Orange Tip butterfly today

May 22nd Saw thirty Swifts this morning flying, swooping and screaming over the housetops and fields.

The water authority has mown the banks of the By Pass Channel, thus cutting down the only surviving Cuckoo Flower before it has had chance to seed.

May 29th Beautiful sunny morning the May Blossom and the Cow Parsley are at their best. Delightful scents fills the air. The May Blossom is quite late this year.[6] W.G. Hoskins puts the date for flowering in the midlands as May 18th and said: 'On that day these miles of snowy hedges reach perfection, so dense and far-reaching that the entire atmosphere is saturated with the bitter-sweet smell whichever way the summer wind is blowing'.
The long trailing water crowfoot in the Erewash is covered with small white flowers.

May Summary
The weather has been particularly wet with the rivers in flood for long periods of time. However there have also been a few hot days when temperatures soared into the seventies.

As the month went on bird sightings dwindled as nesting commenced and birds were busy sitting, vegetation made it harder to see them and less birds were singing in the daytime. This particularly applied to Dunnocks as totals declined from mid month onwards. However, Wren numbers remained constant.

Whitethroat numbers built up to a total of 14 singing males. In 2000 the peak numbers reached 20 in 1999 15, and in 1998 in 18. There seems to be a slight decline in numbers this year. Singing Willow Warblers reached 17 but afterwards declined to 14. In 2000 the total reached 19, in 1999 17, and in 1998 only ten. This species seems to have increased since 1998 but slightly less numbers this year compared to last.

There are at least six Song Thrush territories and probably three pairs of Mistle Thrushes. Three to four pairs of Blackcaps are present and at least two pairs of Chiffchaff. House Sparrow numbers peaked at 88 on 8th but on the 29th only 26 were seen. I think this is due to the species returning to gardens to breed and consequently not being seen in the field areas. A singing Reed Bunting was seen three times in the marshy area of D and hopefully it will breed.

Notable omissions this month have been the lack of any sightings of Kestrels

---

[6] Photo of hawthorn in blossom taken June 2nd 2014

and Sparrowhawks and only two sightings of the Kingfisher. Only one House Martin was seen during the month. The Skylark sang throughout the month and it is hoped that any nesting will survive the farming operations.

June 4th Sunny morning. First Black-headed Gull since 3rd April, but only four Swifts. Hogweed and Elder both in full flower. The Elder is said to be the only tree that the rabbits find distasteful although there is more Elder in the parts of Toton Fields not frequented by Rabbits. Elder gets its name from an Anglo-Saxon word meaning hollow tree.

As the Cow Parsley finishes flowering, the Hogweed takes it place standing tall and erect throughout C and D. Village people carrying bundles of Hogweed to feed their pigs used to be a common sight. Sowerby's "English Botany" says that the sprouting leaves and shoots taste like asparagus. An alternative name 'Cow Parsnip' was a book name invented by William Turner (1548): 'It may be called in Englishe Cow-persnepe or rough Persnepe'

June 5th Lovely sunny morning and quite warm. In E. There are a lot of young Blue Tits calling. In E over 20 House Sparrows in D, an unusual sight is a Collared Dove chasing a Magpie. A Moorhen and 4 Mallards are seen together near the small waterfall. I am pleased to see a Kestrel hovering over D. In May I didn't see one at all. The first young Blackbird of the year seen in C.

As I walk back along the By-Pass Channel I see a Grey Wagtail feeding in the water margins. It is unusual to see a Grey Wagtail here, in June.

Photographs taken in June

Comma	Moorhen & chick	Large Skipper on Mallow
White Campion	Damselfly on blackberry	Blackberry

July 4th As I stand on the Carrfield Avenue Bridge, I am immensely pleased to see a pair of Moorhens in D with five young chicks. A most impressive sight on the corner of the By-Pass Channel as it flows under the main road is a clump of Purple Loosestrife. The purple spikes standing proudly erect by the waterside. Charles Darwin discovered that there are three forms, with flowers differing in the lengths of stamens and styles, and that pollination takes place only when styles receive pollen from stamens of the same length. Pollination is effected by bees.

In the quotation beginning '*There is a willow growing aslant a brook*' Shakespeare referring to the watery grave of Ophelia (Hamlet) mentions long purples. But this description of Ophelia's death garland are, from other hints given, early purple orchids. When John Millais painted the drowning Ophelia in 1851, he chose a similar interpretation, and added a meticulously drawn clump of purple loosestrife beside the dog rose.

In the By-Pass Channel in D are Amphibious Bistort and Common Water Plantain in flower and a few Arrowheads. Near the entrance to C a large amount of Ribbed Melilot is in flower. This plant, and the white variety, which has fewer plants nearby, was originally introduced from Europe as fodder plants. Lucerne, which is widespread on the hillside, is another fodder plant, and was introduced from the Mediterranean about 1650.

Ox-Eye Daisies are still in flower, particularly on the sidings and at the entrance to C. Moon Daisy seems a better name for this flower as it can seem to glow on Midsummer evenings. Field Horsetail is also quite abundant at the entrance to C. Meadow Brown butterflies are everywhere in the grasslands, both the common and darker species. A Red Admiral is also present.

Another prolific flowering plant around the areas is the Common Bird's Foot Trefoil. This species has been endowed with more than seventy local names, a common local name being *Eggs and Bacon*. This name refers to the suffusion of egg-yolk orange and yellow.

July 6th Dull morning after the heat wave of the last few days. A Water Vole is sitting out in the middle of the river in D on top of the floating vegetation. On the path a Hedgehog is trundling along right out in the open.

Five Yellowhammers are in song at the top of C and quite a lot of Dunnock song this morning.

The marsh in C is a mass of Greater Willow Herb which is thriving in the damp area. As you look across the marsh you can see a mass of red flowers, often described as *Codlins-and-Cream*. The name reminds us that Codlins are red-flushed cooking apples, which used to be boiled and eaten with cream. A substantial amount of Reed Mace is also flowering in the area.

On the North Path offshoot quite a lot of Teasel is flowering but I have noticed that the Council have sprayed herbicide on quite a lot of the path verges so they may not survive if is this is repeated. Last year they were mown down when in flower.

Tall plants of Meadow Cranesbill are flowering near the river by the Greenwood centre. Henry Lyte translated a German name for this plant, *Gottesnage,* as Grace of God. Local names include Blue Basins and Blue Buttons.

July 9th A warm sunny morning. Knapweed is very prolific in E and also in C. This plant is also called Hardheads. John Clare described a love-divination game that was played by village girls, using the flower heads:

They pull the little blossom threads
From out the knapweeds button heads
And put the husk wi many a smile
In their white bosoms for awhile
Who if they guess aright the swain
That loves sweet fancys trys to gain
Tis said that ere its lain an hour
Twill blossom wi a second flower
And from her white breasts hankerchief
Bloom as they had ne'er lost a leaf.

The clump of Lady's Bedstraw is flowering again in E. This plant probably derives its name from the old custom of including it in straw mattresses, especially in the beds of women about to give birth. The flower dries to give a scent of new mown hay and when flowering it smells of honey.

Chicory is again flowering in profusion alongside the river in E. This plant has a deeply penetrating tap-root and grows over two feet tall. The sky-blue flowers make an impressive showing along the riverside path.

A Comma Butterfly is in E. Fourteen Magpies on the Park this morning including a number of young.

Greater Burnet, as well as flowering in D is now becoming more common in E. This plant is said to be confined to old damp grasslands, hay meadows and riversides. The plant has beautiful pinnate leaves and dark crimson oblong heads of flowers.

July 10th Bright morning Himalayan Balsam is spreading, it can be seen on both channels of the Erewash in the Park area and also in D. This plant was introduced to gardens from the Himalayas in 1839 and has become widely naturalised along river-banks throughout the country. Its capsules, which contain from four to twelve seeds, are fired off explosively and carried along by water. A medium sized plant will produce some 800 seeds.

The big white Convolvulus (Large Bindweed) plants in E look like fanfares of white trumpets. The more common Field Bindweed flowering at the top of the hill, carpets the grassland like a mass of pink and white candies.

The berries on the Hawthorns look like delivering a very good crop this year.
A solitary Swan in D tries to join two others but gets chased away. Another pair with two cygnet sat on the opposite bank.

July13th Bright morning after overnight rain. A Grey Wagtail is feeding in the By Pass Channel on the Park. There is no sign of the reported young. Two Song Thrushes in E are having a singing duel quite close to each other. Saw ten Mistle Thrushes on the Park this morning, a male and female Chaffinch in the middle of the park and a Collared Dove, both species not usually seen there. Three Mute Swans seen in the main channel on the Park. They seem to have reconciled their differences. Moorhen chick visible this morning and there is one further upstream. It could be part of a fresh brood because an adult is seen nearer the bridge. It is unusual to see a Reed Bunting at the top end of C.

Quite a lot of Tansy flowering in C. This plant was formerly cultivated widely as a pot-herb and as an anthelmintic (*drug that expels worms*) for children. Its much-divided foliage has a strong aromatic odour and the flat-topped golden-yellow flower heads develop brownish ribbed fruits.

A few Mallow plants are flowering in E, but not as many as last year. The leaves, flowers and seeds were all eaten by the Romans, both for food and as a kind of preventative medicine. (Pliny said that a daily dose would make you immune to all diseases).

The Council is busy mowing the verges of all the footpaths and as per last year the Teasels have been cut down.

July17th Warm cloudy morning. On the bank of the By Pass Channel a Mallard was sheltering a number of ducklings. I couldn't see how many. As I came by later I decided to have a further look and found a Mallard with seven ducklings in the main channel. It was possibly the same family although she would have had to take the ducklings under the main road bridges to bring them back to other channel.

The three Mute Swans are together again in D and, at last, a sighting of both the adult Moorhens and their five chicks. In D another Moorhen with a chick is seen and the pair of Mute Swans sitting on the bank with their two cygnets were still present. Next to the Mute Swans is a Mallard with four well grown ducklings, the pen (*female swan*) takes exception to their closeness and half-heartedly makes a small sally at them. The adult female duck bravely stands her ground and places herself between the swan and the ducklings. The swan then sits back down and peace is resumed.

In D a Raspberry bush is full of ripe fruit.

I count a stand of about seventy Greater Mullein, in area 6, the Sidings. The yellow flowers packed on spikes between four and five feet high make an impressive showing. Henry Lyte, 1578 wrote: '*The whole toppe with its pleasant yellow floures sheweth like to a wax candle or taper cunningly wrought*'. A few White Mullein are also in flower.

In the nearby area about three-hundred Evening Primrose plants are in flower. This plant has a very large seed production and seeds can remain viable in the soil for at least forty years.

In the Birch Trees there is a great amount of Rough Hawksbeard making the relative darkness under the birches look like a sea of yellow lanterns.

Common Centaury a beautiful pink flowering plant is giving a very warm colour to the drab grey surroundings of the remnant ballast. The plant was identified with the *Kentaurion* of the Greek medical writers, so named because it was discovered by Chiron the centaur. Centaury had a reputation for controlling fevers in early herbal medicine.

Also growing on the Sidings is a Tea Rose with pinkish/red blooms, and a few Redshank plants. In an area of the Sidings adjacent to C quite a lot of Creeping Cinquefoil is spreading widely in the grass. This is another plant with long history of usage in medicine. Locally, however, the five fingered leaves clearly carved, are frequent among the stone foliage of the chapter house at Southwell Minster, together with other apotropaic plants (*supposedly having the power to avert evil influences or bad luck*), including ivy and hawthorn.

Saw a Small Tortoiseshell Butterfly in D. Found a second Purple Loosestrife in the By Pass Channel in E. Unusual that today I have not seen a single Mistle Thrush. About forty House Sparrows are assembled in the top hedgerow in C at the top of the hill, making a great amount of chatter; they seem to be having a great debate.

This morning I saw the greatest number of Swifts so far this year. Over fifty were flying with exuberant cries and with fantastic aerial displays.

July 20th A Song Thrush is singing and another has been singing in D. The Japanese Knotweed in E is now flourishing again after been cut down by the council late last year. This plant will be very hard to get rid of. Indeed it is now officially regarded as the most pernicious weed in Britain. It was introduced to gardeners in Britain from Japan sometime between 1825 and 1840 and first noticed growing wild in London in 1900. Since then it has colonised almost every part of the country.

A Swallow flies low across the Park as I walk along. I keep looking out for Kingfishers but it is now a couple of months since I last saw one in the area. Pale pink poppies are growing near the Tennis

Courts and another small patch is growing near the Park Bridge and a Teasel is growing near the Tennis Courts.

A young Robin is feeding in E and a Grey Squirrel is in the old willows where the Mill Pond used to be. You can still imagine these willows lining the banks of the pond and their vast boughs lying half-submerged in the water.

There is quite a nice area of Meadowsweet with its cream-coloured inflorescences flowering above the herbage in E and a smaller area in D. The flower emits quite a heady perfume and Gerard in his Herbal of 1597 called this plant *Queen of the Medowe*. However Meadowsweet may have got its name because it was used to flavour mead, hence *mead-sweet*.

Upright Hedge Parsley is in flower like very fine lace.

Speckled Wood and numerous Meadow Brown Butterflies today.

A male Bullfinch flew by as I walked along the path between D and C. Not a common bird for Toton and the first that I have seen for some time. As I walked up to the play-park in C I noticed that the council have drastically flailed the hedgerow and left a jagged mass of stalks and no foliage,

Mignonette, St Johns Wort, Red and White Clover flowering in area 6 and at the corner of D. The solitary Goats Rue is in flower in the same place as last year. This bushy perennial with short sprays of white/purplish-lilac flowers was introduced to this country in the sixteenth century as a vegetable and medicinal herb and later grown for ornament. An old name for the plant was 'French Lilac'.

Toadflax is just coming into flower. This plant was a weed in flax, which looked not unlike flax itself until the flowers developed. So it was named *Linaria (linum,* 'flax') and *Krotenflacks* in German, which William Turner, in 1548, translated into '*todes flax*'.

Wild Carrot is flowering very profusely in several areas including the Sidings and at the top of the hill in C. The vernacular name of this plant 'Birds Nest', is so described by Gerard who says the name was taken into English from the German, and explains how the umbel '*is drawne togither when the seede is ripe, resembling a birdes nest*'. Owing to the curved spine-like projections on the ribs of the fruits these are often spread by animals and by man.

July 31st Cooler, less sunny day after a week of almost constant sunshine and temperatures in the eighties. Heard the first Robin song for some time, this morning; just a very light and brief melody. Marsh Woundwort is flowering on the banks of the By-pass Channel.

In E there is some very tall Rosebay Willow-herb growing up to eight or nine feet in height. Gerard first recorded this plant as a British species in 1597. His description – *'The branches come out of the ground in great numbers, growing to the height of six foote, garnished with brave flowers of great beautie, consisting of fower[1] leaves a piece, of an orien[tal]purple colour. The [seed]pod is long ... and full of downy matter, which flieth away with the winde when the pod is opened'.*

The patch of Purple Loosestrife by the bridge, which looked very sorry for itself after the high water levels, is now almost back to normal with slightly bent flower heads. I see two more of these plants, one in E part of the By Pass Channel and one in E

Mugwort and Wormwood are now in flower; both these plants have rather nondescript flowers. Mugwort, however, does have some attractive features; its leaves are deeply delicately cut, dark green and glistening above, white below. The plant is known throughout Europe as the *Mater Herbarum,* the Mother of Herbs. The evidence for its magical and medicinal reputation dates back to pre-Christian times. Wormwood which grows in close proximity to Mugwort is described as a handsome, silver-leaved perennial. I do not find the 'handsome' description as very apt, I find it be a very dowdy plant. It is a bitter and pungent herb, once used as a worm-dispeller and deterrent. It also provides the bitter principle in absinthe.

A Marsh Hawksbeard is flowering on the banks of the By-pass Channel, and one of the flowers is quite big and attracting up to a ten Hoverflies at a time. A lot of Speckled Wood butterflies about this morning. This species and the Meadow Browns have been quite prolific this year.

On the main channel (park) two Mute Swans with five cygnets are present. During the last few days there have been twelve Mute Swans by the Carrfield Bridge. This morning, however, they have separated into two parties, seven by the bridge and five in D. Next to the five Mute Swans I see the Mallard and her four grown up young, but no sign of the Mallard with the young ducklings, although I did see a Mallard with four young ducklings on the Park Channel about four days ago.

Since the high water levels I haven't seen any of the five young Moorhens that frequented the area west of Carrfield Bridge. However one is present with an adult this morning. I see another young Moorhen under the Sidings Bridge. It is the first time I have noticed a seed head of a Goat's Beard this year. There doesn't seem to have been many flowering this year. On the hillside I see a lot of Lucerne, there seems to be two shades of purple, a light and a dark variety.

At the lower end of the Sidings, some small plants of Hemp Agrimony are in flower. This plant is no relation to either hemp or agrimony. The flowers of this plant have been described as having darker sepals with pink froth over the top, a bit like whipped strawberry mousse. The reddish stems end in

---

[1] fower = four

flowers which have given rise to another common name – Raspberries and Cream. This plant is attractive to many kinds of insects.

A profuse amount of Golden Rod is in flower in C, also Wild Angelica. As I walk through L², I heard a Willow Tit calling, a bird that I haven't seen or heard for some time. Several young Great Tits are flitting through the canopy as I walk by. A few Ox-Eye Daisies are still flowering.

August 2nd Dull, misty morning after overnight rain, gradually warming up into a hot day. As I walk over Carrfield Bridge I see ten Mute Swans and wonder where the other two are. Later I see the twelve together in E.

A Lesser Burdock is flowering in E, as per last year there are only two plants. The seed heads, or burrs, have hooked bristles, which fasten them to any rough surface they come in contact with. The inventor of the Velcro fastener reputedly got his ideas from the seed heads which had attached themselves to his dog's fur. As well as vernacular names such as Sticklebacks and Sticky Bobs, the plant has gained a new name – the Velcro plant.

All the Nettles are in flower. The Nettle has characteristic stinging hairs when seen under a microscope, these exhibit a swollen base, which is really a sac containing an irritant fluid and bearing a tapering stiff tube that ends in a bent portion with a narrow constriction where the walls or impregnated with silica and therefore brittle like glass. When brushed against this tip is broken off, the fractured tube enters the skin, and the consequent pressure upon the sac gives is a hypodermic injection of the poison. The proverbial advice 'to grasp the nettle' is based on the experience that when handled roughly one often suffers far less because the hairs are broken off lower down.

The stinging hairs afford the plant a measure of protection against grazing stock, since they may pierce the thinner-skinned parts of the muzzle. The Nettle has an extensively branched system of yellow roots that, like the stems, are very rough owing to the presence of exceptionally long and strong fibres; in the past these were employed like flax fibres, and produced a most durable textile, an application that was extensively revived during the First World War.

Yarrow (Achillea millifolium) is also flowering along the riverbank and in the Sidings. The plants Latin name comes from the legend that Achilles was said to use it medicinally. The other part of the Latin name means, 'thousand leaf'.

Five Mistle Thrushes on the Park.

Last year I saw far more Hedge Mustard plants and they were far more widely distributed than this year. The only place that there seem to be any plants is the Old Pond Area in E. Here, there are quite a lot. The plants have stiff tangled stems and have given rise to the modern vernacular name of 'barbed-wire plant'.

 In the same area there are a lot of Shepherds Purse plants. If the ripe seeds of this plant be placed in water, a thin layer of mucilage can be seen under the microscope to swell up, and this, together with the flattened shape, ensures ready adhesion to the feet of birds, which also feed upon the seeds; thus dispersal is effected both by internal and external carriage.

---

² L = near the split in the river where the horses ford the river

So far this year I have only noticed a few Bittersweet plants. However I noticed that on the hillside path C there is a whole mass of Bittersweet, sprawling over the hedgerow. This plant otherwise known as Woody Nightshade has purple flowers reflexed behind a yellow cone and at present has many green berries as well as red ones. Gerard describes this plant as: *The flowers be small and somewhat clustered together, consisting of five little leaves (petals) a peece, of a perfect blewe colour with a certaine pricke or yellow pointell in the middle'*

The White Bryony plants are not so obvious this year. this attractive plant is the only native British member of the gourd or cucumber family. The strings of brilliant orange/red berries are dangerously poisonous, but the most toxic parts are the roots, which are mandrake like.

Fewer Spear Thistles about this year. It is an attractive plant and some reach imposing heights and grow in splendid isolation unlike the Creeping Thistle, which is rather dowdy in comparison. I have only seen a couple of Welted Thistles this year.

Nipplewort, seen in E is a plant that will produce nearly 1000 fruits but hasn't been much in evidence this year. Although the milky juice is rather bitter, the plant was formerly used as a salad plant.

In D there is quite a lot of Scentless Mayweed in flower and a small amount of Dove's Foot Cranesbill besides the path. Gerard found Dove's Foot miraculous against ruptures, if it was powdered and drunk in red wine or old claret. He added that if the ruptures were in old persons, the herb should be fortified with the powder of nine red slugs, dried in an oven.

A Common Tern flies gracefully along the river as I walk along. The name Sea Swallow is an apt description of one of the most beautiful and graceful of all sea birds.

As I walk along the top path there are about 50 House Sparrows gathered together in the hedgerow and two Goldfinches fly across the north hillside. As I cross over the sidings-bridge I notice a Moorhen with two young under the next bridge, thankfully they have survived the recent floods.

The path between the two rivers is festooned with thousands of Greater Plantain plants in flower. This path is very well trodden by horses. The plantain leaves are tough, elastic and resilient, and exceptionally tolerant of trampling. This quality, interpreted according to the principles of sympathetic magic, suggested it would be a healing herb for bruises and wounds caused by crushing. As 'waybread' it was included among the Anglo-Saxons' nine sacred herbs:

> *And you, Waybread, mother of worts,*
> *Open from eastward, powerful within,*
> *Over you chariots rolled, over you queens rode,*
> *Over you brides cried, over you bulles belled,*
> *All these you withstood, and these you confounded,*
> *So withstand now the venom that flies through the air,*
> *And the loathed thing which through the land roves.*

August 7th The morning started brightly after heavy rain yesterday but soon turned to rain. The river channels are quite high and there is no sign of the twelve Swans or the five Mallards. However, saw on the calmer waters of the By Pass Channel the pair of Mute Swans and their five cygnets and a Mallard with three young ducklings, are present. A party of young Great Tits is flitting about in E and I hear part of a full song and in the hedgerow there is a large amount of Hops in flower. A mass of Small Tortoiseshell Caterpillars is writhing about on the tips of some nettles at the side of the Park.

As I walk along the riverbank in D I hear then see a family party of Whitethroats, two adults and two young together in a bush and I see a female Blackcap in D. See one Common Hemp Nettle plant in D. This is a plant that was not here last year and like the ones in D newly arrived. Perhaps the winter floods have washed down seed.

As I walk over the hilltop I see about 600 Starlings sitting on the power lines at the bottom end of A.

August 8th Cloudy and windy morning after overnight rain. I walk through my local patch (E) and do not see or hear a single bird. It is now three months since I last saw a Kingfisher (11th May) I keep looking closely at the By Pass Channel for sightings. The wet weather has not helped and if they have bred, the floodwater may have washed any young or eggs away.

Another bird that seems to be an infrequent sight these days, is the Robin. While an odd one is just coming into a very muted short song cycle, I never see or hear more than a couple.

The large white Convolvulus flowers in E before they come into full bloom, have buds that remind

me of pale pinkish tulips. The Mallard with the four grown up ducklings is also in the By Pass Channel. The two Mute Swans with their five cygnets are also present in the same area. This channel with its meandering course and sheltered banks is more of a haven when the water is high than other parts of the rivers system.

Along the banks of the channel there is quite a lot of White Dead Nettle in flower. This plant is known as Adam-and-Eve-in-the-Bower: if you turn the plant upside-down, and beneath the white lip of the corolla, Adam and Eve, the black and gold stamens, lie side by side, like two human figures. Geoffrey Grigson describes the plant as: '*The flowers have a great charm of shape, colour,*
and texture, from the time they lie like soft knobs within the long green teeth of the calx. For one thing, they are not pure white, but white faintly suffused with green. The knob is formed by the upper lip, curled over before its expansion. When it does expand into the hood, look at it with the bare eye or beneath a lens, see how it is felted and fringed with soft white hairs, like a moth'. So the most humble flower, which you can take for granted, can be described poetically.

Also along the By Pass Channel are some Ribwort Plantain plants, I have not seen a lot of this plant this year, unlike the greater variety. This plant was used in a game of 'soldiers'. The stem is wound once round itself, like a noose, just below the head. Then by tightening the noose and pulling it sharply forward, the plantain's head is yanked off and hurled forward like a catapulted stone'.

Some small Red Poppies are flowering along the banks of the By-pass Channel, plus quite a lot of Hedge Mustard. I thought that this latter plant had almost disappeared, this year, but it has now become quite prolific. A Squirrel is near the pavilion as I walk by; this is the second time that I have seen it near here.

August 10th Bright, sunny morning after heavy rain yesterday. The Swifts appear to have departed. I shall miss their screaming aerobatic displays. I find another Red Goosefoot plant along the banks of the By Pass Channel. The other one is on the arable field at the top of the hill.

The Mountain Ash trees are showing a prolific harvest of berries, at first they are orange then turn to red. This Rowan tree has been widely planted as part of the conditions of the housing development, and not planted, as it used to be, as a protection of the houses against witches.

A lot of Poppies are in flower along the margins of arable field. It is not very often, nowadays, that you see Poppies in cereal crops, but for thousands of years, corn and poppy and civilisation have gone together. The Assyrians respectfully named it 'Daughter of the Field'; in Greece it was the flower of Aphrodite as goddess of vegetation, and the Romans looked on it as sacred to their corn goddess, Ceres, who taught men to sow and reap, thresh and winnow.

White Marsh Thistle is flowering again in C. The white variety is a rarity.

Blue Fleabane, like a miniature Michaelmas Daisy plant is flowering on the sidings. The flower is not really blue, its flower heads are pale purple at the rim and pale yellow in the centre. Long tufts of fine white hairs, ringed with red, form on each fruiting head, eventually serving as parachutes to disperse seeds. These give the plant the botanical name of *Erigeron*, from the Greek *eri,* 'early', and *geron,* 'old', because its white beard suggests premature old age. The common name of fleabane refers to the burning of the plant in the past to smoke out fleas.

One area of the sidings contains a large patch Hares Foot Clover. This plant derives its name from the soft downy heads of the flowers, which have the shape and texture of a hare's foot.

I am pleased to see, as I stand on the Sidings Bridge, a Moorhen chick with its parent, feeding under the next bridge.

Quite a lot of Meadow Vetchling is in flower. The numerous yellow flowers are visited mainly by bumble bees, which have tongues long enough to reach the nectar at the bottom of the long flower tube. The shape of the flowers has earned the plant the folk-name of 'lady's slippers'

Great Mullein is still flowering. Its tall, straight flower spikes with individual flowers held close to the stem, have a staff like appearance, and given rise to the alternative name of 'Aaron's Rod'. The downy, white coating on the leaves is made up of innumerable tiny-branched hairs. Long before the introduction of cotton to Britain, this fluffy layer was scraped off and made into candlewicks. At country gatherings, the entire stem was burnt as a flare. The folk–names 'candlewick plant' and 'high taper' derive from these uses.

August 13th Bright, windy morning after heavy rain yesterday. I was awakened about half-past five this morning by the sound of Canada Geese calling. I quickly looked out of the window and saw a skein of 16 flying westwards.

The Common Hemp Nettle in E is spreading and is a very vigorous plant. In common with Hemp Agrimony, hemp nettle was so named because of the apparent similarity of its leaves to those of Indian hemp.

In E a Marsh Ragwort is in flower and a large patch of Bladder Campion is also flowering at the end of the track. White Campion is also flowering on the hillside in C. Its show of white blossoms has been called summer saucers and the plant is very attractive to moths at night.

White Clover is a very common plant around Toton Fields and

seems to be on nearly every pathway and grassland. The Red Clover is far less common. Of the two the Red Clover flowers are far more attractive than the white.

The By Pass Channel and its banks keep on providing new plants. Branched Bur-reed has appeared, although one or two plants did show near the bund in D last year. Redshank (*Persicaria macularia*) has now spread right along the banks and is very attractive to look at with its red stems and pink flowers. A Fat Hen plant has also appeared.

In E Knotgrass (*Polygonum aviculare*) is very prolific along the sides of the path. Both its common and botanical names refer to the knotty swellings where each leaf joins the stem, hence *Polygonum,* which is derived from two Greek words meaning 'many knees'. The species name *aviculare* means 'small bird' and comes from the fact that sparrows and finches often feed on the seeds. Another plant along the By-pass Channel is Wall Lettuce and quite a lot of tall Rough Hawksbeard.

I see a fully-grown young Moorhen out on the park downstream of Carrfield Bridge. This is a welcome sight as it shows at least one has survived the July storms.

Very few Welted Thistles around but alongside the main channel on the park quite a big plant is growing. However it is starting to sprawl because of its own weight and the recent heavy rainfall. Most of the Creeping Thistles have finished flowering and have turned to seed. What was once a bright show of purple flowers has now turned to dull, dowdy and scruffy, brown seed heads.

At the field margin in E there is a beautiful clump of Upright Hedge Parsley with flowers of pink, white and purple and full of Hoverflies. This plant is said to be one of nature's 'hitch hikers' as it spreads its seeds by tiny hooked bristles.

At the small beach next to the S bend in the river, in D a Grey Wagtail is present as I walk by. The Grey Wagtail can now be said to be a Toton resident as it has been present throughout the breeding season.

On the hillside path in C, numerous leaves of Cut-leaved Crane's-bill have appeared all the way up to the top of the hill. These plants will survive throughout the winter and some of the leaves turn an attractive red colour brightening an otherwise drab winter scene.

Teasels are beginning to turn a pinkish purple, which I find extremely attractive to look at in close proximity. These conical flower heads are extremely attractive to bees and hoverflies. The dry prickly head was used to comb or tease the cloth to raise the nap in the textile industry, hence a nickname brushes and comb, or fullers teasel.

On the arable field I find Good King Henry. Although this plant has an English sounding name it is a translation of the German *Guter Heinrich,* or 'Good Henry'. The word 'King' was added in this country.

Hop Trefoil is flowering well in various places in C and in area 6. This plant is very similar to Black Medick, which is flowering in C. The name 'Medick' has nothing to do with medicine, it is derived from the 'Plant of the Medes' an ancient Middle Eastern people.

White Melilot is now quite widespread in the Sidings and is growing quite tall and often straggly. Melilots were introduced into this country as fodder plants in the sixteenth century, although other sources state that they were introduced by herbalists, who used them to make ointments and poultices to reduce swellings, blisters and bruises. Melilots are a rich source of wild honey, and are commonly pollinated by Hoverflies and bees. Nearby I find some more Goats Beard seed heads.

On the Sidings there are numerous plants of Herb Robert. The 'robert' of the plants name is believed to be a corruption of the Latin *ruber* meaning red, although there are many other derivations. The plant also has far more vernacular names than almost all other plants. This is because it is so well known and has lived side-by-side with man for centuries. Gerard describes it as: '*Herbe Robert groweth on old wals, as well those made of bricke and stone, as those of mudde and earth: it groweth likewise among rubbish, in the bodies of trees that are cut downe, and in moist and shadowie ditch banks'*. Wordsworth found Herb Robert to be an attractive plant and wrote: 'Poor Robin is yet flowerless, but how gay with his red stalks on this sunny day'.

A Mute Swan is preening under the Sidings Bridge, but no sign of the big party or the pair with cygnets. Since the nineteenth century the word 'mute' has been applied, but the name 'swan' is an Anglo-Saxon word meaning 'sounder'. The Mute Swan is not mute and it gives a deep hiss when angered and has a trumpeting grunt and growls. However the word 'sounding' as applied to this species refers to the strange and beautiful soughing of its wings when it flies. One of the Riddle poems of the Exeter book, translated by Richard Hamer, describes the wing music:

> *My dress is silent when I tread the ground*
> *Or stay at home or stir upon the waters*
> *Sometimes my trappings and the lofty air*
> *Raise me above the dwelling place of men.*
> *And then the power of clouds carries me far*
> *Above the people; and my ornaments*
> *Loudly resound, send forth a melody*
> *And clearly sing, when I am not in touch*
> *With earth or water, but a flying spirit'.*

Greater Burnet is now flowering well on the south side of the By Pass Channel in D. As mentioned earlier in this diary Greater Burnet is spreading well into other areas this year.

This month, so far, has been one of very few bird sightings. Everywhere seems bereft of the common species of birds such as the Dunnock, Robin, Greenfinch, Chaffinch and Tits. The thick vegetation hides many birds but there doesn't seem to be many flying about. Bird song is almost over, a few Wrens can be heard singing and the odd Greenfinch and Robin, but otherwise silence. It may be they are replacing flight feathers.

At the top end of C twelve Collared Doves are sitting on the telephone wires above the cereal crop. They occasionally fly down to the crop and then return to the wire.

At the side of the path in C, next to the tall hedgerow, I see a small plant with a tiny yellow flower with four petals. On close examination it turns out to be Black Mustard. This plant is solitary and there is no sign of any more. It makes one wonder how it came to grow in that particular place.

August 14th In the Erewash, just above Carrfield Bridge a Mallard and three grown up ducklings are feeding alongside the water margins. This group is younger than the other Mallard with the four ducklings. In the same area there is an adult Moorhen crossing over water. As I walk along the flood bank in E, I come across about fifty House Sparrows in the garden hedgerow. This is the most that I have ever seen in this area.

Indeed, today, I see 120 House Sparrows in Toton Fields. Walking across the park I notice a Cormorant flying over. This is the first one I have seen in the area since the 25th April. As I walk along the banks of the By Pass Channel, I keep expecting to find something new and each day I seem to be rewarded. I am not disappointed as I see a new Purple Loosestrife growing. I shall enjoy this plant for the next month or more as the one near the bridge is now past its best. One solitary Red Poppy has also appeared in the same area and another wriggling mass of Small Tortoiseshell butterfly caterpillars on a patch of nettles. They don't seem to spread out over the whole nettle but concentrate on the tops.

On the main channel, the two Mute Swans with their five cygnets are feeding. As I mentioned yesterday the Swan is not mute, these are having low-pitched contact calls as they feed. Below the bridge two Mallards are feeding. A Black-headed Gull is flying over the park and I notice that it has almost lost its black head. I have missed seeing the Mistle Thrushes on the park and I am pleased to see one here today.

As I walk along the bank of the river in D I hear a Moorhen calling and getting as close as I can I see one perched on a low branch overhanging the river. The bird is calling to a young one hiding under the low bushes at the water's edge. The young one swims out and downstream and I notice another adult close by. Perhaps the young one is a survivor of the original five young ones that were in this area before the July storms. As I walk further up stream I come across two more adult Moorhens, in D. Under the Sidings Bridge there is yet another young one.

There are a number of big brown dragonflies flying over the river today and surprise, surprise, I see a Kingfisher! The first that I have seen since May.

I hear a very muted Willow Warbler song and find a few groups of Pale Toadflax, *Linaria repens.* These have lilac-coloured flowers and the plants are a lot smaller than the Common Toadflax. There are several Buddleias growing in the area including a dwarf specimen.

The St Johns Wort, as it turns to seed, produces some lovely red seed pods; it is almost like another flowering plant. Some very small Broad Leaved Willowherbs are flowering among the ballast; they have exquisite pink flowers. Great Willow Herb is flowering profusely.

As I walk through the denser patches of Birch, Buddleia and Broom, I come across little clearings where smaller plants are in flower. In one of these I find a group of Wild Parsnips with beautiful

yellowish/green flower bracts and seed heads. In E there are some Asparagus plants. I have not seen these here before. I do not know whether it is of a wild variety as this is supposed to be confined to Cornwall and Pembrokeshire.

In the past wild plants had a more prominent place in people's lives than they do now. They were not only givers of food, but they were providers of medicine and had magical properties. While plants had common names each plant had a variety of local names and these reflected local usage or customs. Finding out the non-technical histories of wild plants and their usage is just as exciting as knowing why a plant grows in a particular place. The technical names of plants are also very interesting and these often reflect historical personages or events. *The Red Dead Nettle for example also known as the bumble bee flower or bad man's posies, has a latin name lamina meaning devouring monster. This refers to the helmet shape of the flower giving the impression of open jaws. The red dead nettle was a medicinal plant with a variety of uses. It's dried leaves were used as a poultice to stem heavy bleeding. The leaves were also made into a tea to promote perspiration when treating chills.*

Finding different wild plants in Toton Fields has been like a voyage of discovery, particularly in a folklore and poetical sense.

August 17th Bright, sunny morning after heavy rain the day before. As I stand on the Carrfield Bridge I see a solitary Mute Swan waiting expectantly. On the Park the wet grass is shining in the sunlight with millions water droplets. Having walked through C recently without seeing a bird, this morning I see on one of the paths that there are five Blackbirds and three Dunnocks feeding. The Hawthorn berries are just beginning to turn red and the bushes are quite heavily laden.

At the top of C a couple of Willow Warblers are calling with faint contact sounds. At the top of C there is a tree with small green fruits similar to greengages. Nearby a Great Tit is attempting a full 'teacher, teacher song'.

September 10th After a long break I am now continuing my walks around Toton Fields. A bright cloudy morning. Toadflax is flowering in various places today and is growing quite tall. Robins are now into their autumn songs, rather sweet but somewhat plaintive and weak. The Japanese Knotweed is now in flower making quite a display. Moles have become active on the Park and it is quite a time since I last saw a fresh molehill. The Erewash is extremely low and in some places parts of the main river are only a few inches or so deep. The By Pass channel is only a mere trickle. The river is quite a pretty sight as the sunlight is reflected on the pebble bed.

A solitary Mute Swan swims up to me as I walk by in D', no doubt seeking a hand out. Also in the same area is a pair of Mute Swans with five grown up cygnets, these Swans also swim up to me as I stand on the riverbank. Elderberries are very profuse and hanging in dark succulent clusters from every branch. A second pair of Mute Swans, with two grown up cygnets, are resting on the riverbank, in D.

As I walk along the path in D, I hear a Green Woodpecker 'yaffling' from C. This is the first time I have heard this bird since the spring. Where does it go during the summer? In C there are nine Magpies seeming to have a quite talkative meeting on the pylon. At the side of the path in C, a Crab Apple tree has lovely rosy red apples brightly reflecting the sunlight and nearby a prolific display of rose hips. Two complementary colours brightening the hillside.

The Hawthorns are full of thousands of red berries, a great treat in store for the early winter bird populations.

In the marsh (C) there are seventy spikes of Reed Mace making quite an impressive display.

As I walk over Carrfield Bridge I see a Kingfisher sitting in the hedgerow and as I pass by it flies swiftly upstream. I counted 80 House Sparrows this morning and well over 600 Starlings.

September 11th Bright but cloudy morning. A few Speckled Wood butterflies about this morning but quite small in size and a pair of mating Dragonflies flew by in E.

Above the farm in A, three Magpies are mobbing a Raven. The Raven ducks and dives to escape the attentions of the Magpies and eventually has to settle in the top of a tree. The Magpies still continue to swoop on it before flying off and leaving the bird alone. While the Raven was flying it kept putting its feet out and back. This is the second time that I have seen a Raven in Toton this year, the last time was on the 4th June in E. This bird flew northwards across the Park. The call of the Raven reminds me of Macbeth saying -*The raven himself is hoarse, that croaks the fatal entrance of Duncan under my battlements.*

 As I walk home along the path in D a Sparrowhawk circles overhead and then flies towards the Sidings.

September 12th Bright morning but rather cloudy. 3 Collared Doves near the Tennis Courts is an unusual event. They don't normally frequent this area. On the Park over a1000 Starlings are feeding on the grass. As I neared Carrfield Bridge, a Kingfisher flies along the main channel from the Park northwards.

Near the Oak tree in D, the river, for two-thirds of its width, is only about an inch deep. In Mallard Reach there is a Mute Swan and 4 cygnets. One of the adults is missing and also one of the cygnets. I search the whole length of the Erewash from the sidings to the A 6005 but no sign of the missing birds. Very unusual! The second pair of Swans plus the 2 cygnets, are still in D.

This is turning out to be a Starling morning, in addition to the large number on the Park there are about another 150 in D. The Green Woodpecker calls as I walk up the C path and at the end of D, a Whitethroat flits about in the hedgerow.

September 17th Bright but cool windy morning. Two Chaffinches in D area are a welcome surprise after not seeing any at all for some time. The arable fields have been harvested and this has attracted a number of Carrion Crows – 28 this morning. One field is being ploughed but as this has only just started it has yet to attract the normal flock of Gulls.

September 21st Bright sunny and quite warm morning. In D where the path verges were sprayed and then severely mown, numerous plants of Common Mallow and Common Field Speedwell have appeared. On the top of the Green (top of Banks Road) there are five Blackbirds, a Song Thrush and five Magpies feeding. Another two Blackbirds are bathing in the Erewash. It is not very often that birds are seen frequenting this Green. Perhaps the recently mown grass favours their search for food, small insects, seeds and the like.

At the confluence of the By Pass Channel and River Erewash, there are the two adult Mute Swans and their two cygnets are present. Also at the confluence a Teasel stands on the river bank. I find another Asparagus plant in E and a large stand of Amphibious Bistort in D. New Cut Leaved Cranesbill plants are showing well in the path margins in E.

Along the top hedgerow a flock of a dozen Long-tailed Tits are foraging and flit about calling softly and musically. Nearby a Yellowhammer is singing.

 Not a lot of flowers in bloom at present. The most prevalent are Red Clover, Toadflax, Yarrow, Birds Foot Trefoil, and Lucerne.

September 25 misty morning after overnight rain. As I walk over Carrfield Bridge, three Jackdaws fly overhead calling as they fly. This bird is a rare sight in Toton. At the Sidings Bridge the two cygnets are alone and there is no sign of the adults.

In D there are nine Robins singing this morning. As I walk along the Sidings path in D, a Heron alights quite close to me and seems unperturbed by my presence. As I walk back along the By Pass Channel a Grey Wagtail flies upstream showing it brilliant yellow undersides.

September 26th Bright sunny morning after foggy start. This is a cobweb morning, as the heavy dew indicated their presence, everywhere seems to be festooned with them, both the vertical and horizontal varieties. Without the dampness you would not realise that hundreds of spiders are present.

At the confluence a Chiffchaff is singing at the top a Hawthorn bush. Starlings seem to spend a lot of time sitting on the overhead power lines or on the pylons. As they sit they seem to be having numerous conversations with each other and this is quite a pleasant sound.

Recently I haven't seen many finches, but this morning the hedgerow in C has at least 12 Greenfinches, 4 Chaffinches and two Goldfinches. I even see a Coal Tit on the hilltop; this is an extremely rare sight.

A Small Tortoiseshell butterfly is feeding on the clover at the top of the hill and I hear the Green Woodpecker calling as I walk past E.

Last year was an exciting year of discovery in recording the wild plants of Toton. This year I have added a few more to the list but I have the feeling that I have either missed some that were present last year, or that they have disappeared.

Certainly there was only one surviving plant of Lady's Smock, these plants fall victim of the Environment Agency's mowing regime before they can seed.

Members of the Buttercup family of plants were noticeably in short supply and Hairy Tare, a prolific plant last year seemed to be totally missing. Cleavers is another plant that was prolific last year but very sparse this. Only one Hedge Woundwort plant grew last year and that was cut down by the council before it could seed. It has not appeared this year.

Some of the plants added to last year's list include Marsh Hawkweed, Marsh Woundwort, Marsh Ragwort, Lupin, Red Goosefoot, Wild Parsnip and Black Mustard.

One plant that is spreading quite fast is Himalayan Balsam.

It is too much to expect that Toton harbours any rare species, but what we have is very interesting, and, as I have said earlier in this diary, some species are quite prolific and others have a mere toe-hold. It will be interesting in future years to monitor the changes in flora as the recently planted woodlands mature and changes to river management alter the composition of aquatic and riverside species. Changes will also affect bird species and populations.

October 6th Twelve Goldfinches today feeding on the thistles and forty Linnets on the arable fields. Only sixteen House Sparrows seen today, which is the second lowest total since I began recording. It seems strange that in August I counted over a hundred one-day and now they are down to such low levels.

October 11ᵗʰ Bright, sunny morning and quite warm. On the arable fields there are over a hundred Wood Pigeons feeding; a large proportion of them being young ones.

A Red Admiral butterfly flies past as I walk along the path. The modern name of this butterfly evolved from the 18ᵗʰ century given name of 'admirable' so called because of its bright colours. In the autumn the Red Admiral is a visitor to Ice-plants, Buddleia and Michaelmas daisies. In the wild it feeds on the nectar of teasel, Scabious, Clover and the flowers of Ivy. It also flocks to windfall apples rotting on the ground– a scene captured by William Wordsworth in his poem To a butterfly: '*This plot of orchard-ground is ours.*'

Three Grey Wagtails this morning on the By-pass Channel, two on the bund area and by the park.

October 16ᵗʰ Bright day. Another sighting of a Grey Wagtail feeding on the bund area and the dozen Goldfinches are still present. Two separate pairs of Mallards are present on the main channel, one pair of females and a male/female pair.

October 17ᵗʰ Cloudy/bright morning. Chicory is still flowering in E Three Jackdaws flew over the park calling as they passed. It is very rare to see Jackdaws in Toton, and they are seldom seen on the ground. Sometimes they can be heard and seen as they pass over early in the morning with parties of Rooks flying to their feeding grounds.

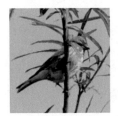

Sixty Linnets today on the arable fields, feeding in a flock. When disturbed they fly up together, swirl round and resettle.

October 22ⁿᵈ On the arable field, which has recently had a crop of broad beans, over 1800 Wood Pigeons are feeding, together with over 150 Linnets. I walked onto the field and found the ground strewn with beans, some sprouting.

October 23ʳᵈ Heavy overnight rain leading to a rather dull morning. The river is almost at the top its banks on both channels. Everywhere is saturated and muddy. It is nice to see two Mistle Thrushes on the Park after a long absence. A Moorhen shows itself on the Park near Carrfield Bridge. Again this is a very welcome sight after two months of not seeing one in this area. There is also another Moorhen in D. As I walk up towards the Sidings I hear the Green Woodpecker calling but fail to see it.

I see a Red Admiral butterfly in E plantation; this is the second one that I have seen this week.

Still a large number of Wood Pigeons on A, but less than half the number of the day before (800). Blackbird numbers have also halved from the previous days total.

October 24ᵗʰ On the Bowling Green a Pied Wagtail is feeding. Other birds do not seem to find the very short grassy sward to their liking but Pied Wagtails can often be seen here. Red Clover is still in flower on the Sidings and in E. This is about the only plant still flowering apart from an odd Daisy and Dandelion. It is nice to see the bright bits of colour in an otherwise drab scene. Wood Pigeon numbers have risen, over 1200 this morning on the bean fields.

I am still wondering why there should be two plants in Toton that have produced white flowers, when normally they would produce purple ones. The first, Centaurea nigra – Knapweed, produced white flowers apparently from the same clump of plants flowering on the hillside. There did not seem to be any difference, apart from the colour of the flowers, between the plants with purple flowers and those with white ones. Centaurea jacea is known to produce white flowers on occasion, but this plant is a rare alien mostly found in the south of England. While it is known to hybridise with Centaurea nigra it soon disappears.

The plant producing white flowers for the second year in succession is the Marsh Thistle, one plant being found in E. It will be interesting to see if any more white flowers appear next year.

October 25th Keats in his 'Ode to Autumn' describes the period as:

> *Season of mists and mellow fruitfulness,*
> *Close bosom-friend of the maturing sun;*

October 29th Dull morning. On the bean field the numbers of Wood Pigeons have reduced to 300, but today, in the same area, there are 30 Fieldfares, 350 Starlings, 200 Linnets and a Jay, a new bird, for me, at Toton Fields.

As I walk back along the By-pass Channel in E I see a Moorhen; it is not very often that they frequent this channel. I am extremely pleased to see three Moorhens on the park, one at the west end and two at the east end, plus a Kingfisher at the Willow Bend on the By Pass Channel. This is the first Kingfisher that I have seen since the 12th September. Today saw the highest total of House Sparrows for this month – 52.

October 31st Fine sunny morning but a very poor morning bird wise, only sixteen species. Of these species numbers are well down apart from 22 Pied Wagtails on the arable field (bean field). This field has been mostly ploughed during the last couple of days and the large numbers of Linnets, Wood Pigeons and Starlings have departed.

The Robin song which has been very widespread throughout the first three weeks of the month has ended. Only three Robins were heard this morning and only from calls and not from song. No Yellowhammers have been seen since the 6th but a Reed Bunting is present this morning in C.

November **5th** Bright but cold morning. Two juvenile Moorhens on the west end of the Park and an adult near Carrfield Bridge in D. This is the first time that I have seen any young Moorhens since 17th August.

Some Red Clover is still in flower, which could possibly provide a little nectar for late insects. Red berries while duller still add colour to a winter scene. Another bright colour in the same area is the sight of four Bullfinches as they flit between the hawthorn bushes.

November 6th Cloudy, but not so cold as yesterday. As I walk along the Twitchell in D. I hear then see four Long-tailed Tits flying along in front of me. Still a few Toadflax flowering in C and in E Yarrow and Large Convolvulus is still in flower. A few Dandelions are still out and on one I saw a Honey Bee.

The arable field is now completely ploughed and a nearby one is being harrowed until a fine tilth. Here there are 40 Feral Pigeons, 34 Pied Wagtails and 30 Black-headed Gulls. Along C hedgerow I see a couple of Yellowhammers, the first for some time. As I walk along the hilltop a Kestrel flies over, quite high. This is the first Kestrel that I have seen in the area since 5th June.

November 18th Dull, slightly misty calm morning. As I walk through D, a Kingfisher flies swiftly downstream. In a short stretch of D hedgerow 24 Blackbirds are feeding on the Hawthorn berries and a couple of Fieldfares appear in the vicinity.

On the north path in C 16 Blackbirds are feeding and in total, today, I see 83 Blackbirds, the highest total this year, an obvious influx of continental birds. Last year, in November, the highest count was 179. Also at the top of the hill I see six Yellowhammers and 18 Greenfinches. Out in the open in E I see two Moorhens feeding out in the open and a Pied Wagtail on the Bowling Green again.

November 19th Bright, warm and sunny morning. The trees look stunning this morning with various shades of green, gold, brown and yellow.

On the top path in E a Green Woodpecker is feeding on the ground and as I moved up it flew onto a telegraph post and hid out of sight. It is an interesting fact that when bird watching being in the right place at the right time is an important factor. Earlier on during my morning's walk I was stopped by a couple and engaged in conversation. If I had not been stopped would I have still seen the woodpecker? Who knows?

As I walked along the path through the arable fields I was thinking of the summer song of the Skylark that I often heard in this area. Then as I walked on a Skylark flew over, a happy coincidence.

November 26th A Heron is standing on the bank of the By Pass Channel in E and suddenly with a swift stab of its beak it spears a Vole and quickly swallows it.

November 28th More Blackbirds about this morning (79) although the Hawthorn berries are fast disappearing. It has also been a good morning for Greenfinches, I have seen twenty in C.

As I walk to the top end of E, I see 8 Goldfinches, 2 Bullfinches and 2 Chaffinches flitting about the bushes. The Goldfinches are calling softly to each other in musical voices.

The Anglo-Saxons of the eighth century called the Goldfinch *Thisteluige* or Thistle-tweaker. The association with the thistle plant is ancient and widespread; the Latin name for thistle is *Carduus* and today this forms the first part of the scientific name for a genus of thistles which includes the musk thistle. The scientific name of the Goldfinch, *Carduelis carduelis,* is also derived from the same Latin name.

I only very occasionally see Bullfinches in Toton, and nationally, according to the CBC Index 1972-96 they have declined by 62% and by 27% in the BBS index 1994-98. The first written appearance of Bullfinches occurs in Chaucer's *The Romaunt of the Rose.* He describes them as Alpes. *Alpes* is the

oldest name we know for Bullfinch and it still exists in various forms such as Olf, Hoop and Mawp. Michael Drayton (1612) in his poem – Polyolbion, describes the Bullfinch as a '*Nope*'. This name still exists in Shropshire and Staffordshire. Ian Newton in his study of finches has shown that when the seeds of nettle, dock, bramble and ash are plentiful, Bullfinches tend to ignore the buds of fruit, but in years where the seed stocks give out before the end of winter, they will turn to orchards.

Today I recorded the lowest Dunnock total that I have ever recorded – one. In the spring I regularly counted over 30 Dunnocks and the highest total was 36. I am quite worried about the decline in numbers of this bird locally.

December 4th Bright sunny morning. River over the bund[3]. In the first part of D quite a few Hawthorn berries are left and these are being feasted on by about 10 Blackbirds and 2 Redwings. Almost all the leaves are off the trees now and the colourful period is over. A lot of Robin song this morning and a couple of Great Tits singing as well. Catkins out on a bush in C.

Nice to see a Song Thrush in C the first one that I have seen in Toton since September, and then only one. Previous to this the last time that I saw a Song Thrush was August 2nd.

Over the arable fields a Sparrowhawk is being mobbed by three Carrion Crows. I do not see Sparrowhawks very often and this one is only the fifth occurrence this year in Toton.

On the By Pass Channel in D, a juvenile Mute Swan is eating grass from the side of the bank. At the top end of E it is unusual to see five Dunnocks together in one bush.

December 15th Bright morning with slight frost overnight. See two Moorhens on the park and a Kingfisher flying swiftly upstream in D.

Moles are very active in D, numerous mole hills beside the path. A Snowberry tree is growing on the banks of the river in C, I think it is self-set. A Mistle Thrush is singing in E. There is a high number of Blackbirds this morning (67) and Great Tits (13).

December 17th Cloudy morning and warmer than of late. A male Bullfinch comes down to drink and a Song Thrush alights next to it. After seeing this Song Thrush I see four more making a total of five in D, a record! The Green Woodpecker is calling as I walk through D and a rare sight a Grey Squirrel in the same area. Quite a lot of Daisies are in flower on the north slopes of C.

December 19th Cold bright red sunny morning. Quite a lot of Long-tailed Tits around. There were at least two parties of ten in each. A Grey Wagtail graces the main river bank as I walk through C. High number of Robins today (32). Carrion Crows are very vocal at daybreak it is like they are playing a Game of Crows. Buzzards are coming to be a regular sight as they fly over the reserve.

December 31st As I walked up to Carrfield Bridge I saw a Kingfisher fly swiftly upstream. I have not seen a Kingfisher many times this year at Toton but it is very rewarding to see one on the first and last days of the year. On the park side of Carrfield Bridge a Mallard and three Teal are feeding nearby.

A flock of thirty Goldfinches are feeding on the Alder catkins in C and as they fly they make a musical tinkling sound as they call to each other. A flock of a dozen Greenfinches are present in E and together with other small parties twenty-four are counted in the whole area. I hear two Dunnocks singing this morning together with several Robins and a very muted song of a Great Tit. A first year Moorhen is feeding on the bank of the Erewash in E. Towards dusk seven Blackbirds, a Song Thrush and a Robin are feeding in the garden.

 I have enjoyed writing this diary as I will be able to look back and picture the sites and scenes over and over again. This ends the diary.

Photographs Karen Barker, Gillian Morral, Norman Lewis, Peter & Jane Klymowskyj

---

[3] Step in the river bed causing a mini waterfall over the step.

Bibliography

Crawford, Peter –   Living Britain ,
Greenoak, Francesca –   British Birds – Their Folklore, Names, and Literature
Lord Grey of Falladon – The Charm of Birds
Grigson, Geoffrey –   The Englishman's Flora
Mabey, Richard –   Flora Britannica
Mead, Chris –   The State of the Nations' Birds
Munsterberg, Peggy (Edited by) The Penguin Book of Bird Poetry
Sir Edward, Salisbury – Weeds and Aliens
Peter Marren –   Britains' Rare Flowers

River Erewash, Blackthorn in Compartment A

Sports Field, rough grassland margins in Compartment A

Wildlife – Historical changes

Many factors affect wildlife populations such as habitat and weather, but the most significant is probably man's influence on the land. Agriculture, industry and housing developments have all played a part in changing the composition of the wildlife in Toton. Weather will also have made an impact, the days of the severe winters, deep snow and hard frosts appear to have gone but there is little data on this aspect, in particular with regard to the influence weather has had on the wildlife.

Agriculture

Documentary evidence from estate accounts, rent books and newspaper reports can only give a glimpse into the wildlife in the area as no account or list of species exists from earlier centuries. Toton for centuries has been an

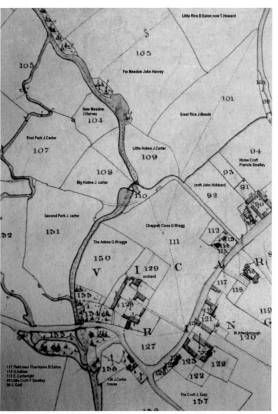

Tithe map extract 1847

agricultural Manor. Farming has therefore been an integral part of Toton's life, with a mix of pasture, meadow and arable lands. Woodland would also have been an important resource for the owners of Toton Manor.

The 17th century was a period of change from medieval farming to enclosure with the planting of hedges and creation of smaller fields. These hedges would have provided extra habitats for many creatures. Accounts of expenses in the rental books show the kinds of game bought from the market or local trader. Sir John Stanhope of Elvaston owned Toton manor at this time. Some items listed in the accounts were purchased at markets and others from named men possibly local people or merchants. Some items were exotic, such as lobster, oyster and plaice (1629) which must have been bought at a market or fair.

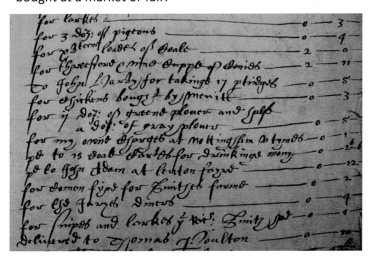

Other items such as rabbits and small birds could have been caught locally. In 1620 larks, pigeons, partridges, green plover, grey plover and snipe are part of the expenses paid for from the Toton Manor at Michaelmas (September 29th). They were bought in large quantities – 3 dozen pigeons, 3 score and nine conies (rabbits) and 2 dozen green plovers (lapwings). One can speculate whether this was for a special occasion or could be stored perhaps in an ice house for use over a longer period. A reference some twenty years later (1642) accounts for snipe, woodcock, blackcock, partridge, mallard and widgeon.

8 snipes on(e) bilcock (blackcock) i woodcock	2s 8d
3 p[a]rtrigie & 9 p triges (partridge)more cost	6s 6d
One duck & a mallard cost	2s 6d
6 cockes cost (woodcock or blackcock?)	5s
2 cockes more cost	18d
2 mallard 2 wigeon & indcock cost	22d (1s 10d)

One notable absentee is pheasant. This ground feeding bird, does not appear to be widespread in the 17[th] century and perhaps became a table bird after the development of guns for shooting parties and the breeding of these game birds. By the 19th century it is recorded in Toton when the land was owned by Richard Birkin (Lace manufacturer, Mayor of Nottingham 1861-3).

During the latter part of 19th century saw gamekeepers living in Toton protecting the pheasants and other game birds from poachers. An example of such an illegal activity, is that of the case of Richard Eaton, Isaac Hooley (Long Eaton) and James Cross who were caught at 2 a.m. in the barley field with nine pheasants and a number of nets (August 1885).[1] At the court appearance they were sentenced to three months with hard labour.

Toton was an agricultural Manor until the early 20th century. In 1892, a sale document lists the estate as comprising the village of Toton, farmhouses, cottages and 1165 acres of land including the Manor of Toton, fishery and ferry. It names Toton's farms as The Coneries, Manor House farm, Hill farm, Mill farm, and Toton Fields farm. Other farms such as Grange, farm, Ferry farm and Whyatt's farm were not using these names at that time. Later (1930s) the Co-op farm took over a large area of land west of Stapleford Lane.

Trees were a valuable commodity. Spinneys and plantations marked on the 1847 tithe map must have been a resource for wildlife as well as humans. Many properties had orchards. Manor House farm, tenanted by John Harby included an orchard whose size was 3 roods 5 poles (nearly 1 acre). This is just one orchard among many. The names of the fields gives some idea of the shape and content including some trees for example Oak tree close (tenant John Herrick) ,) and   Wet Grass Close (18 acres, tenant Henry Wallis 1831)

Rabbits brought by the Normans, occupied sandy areas (warrens), grazed on the nearby herbage. Hares a native species were once living in the area as

> TOTON : GAME TRESPASS.
> *George Adcock* was charged with being found on enclosed land at Toton, in pursuit of game, having a dog with him at the time, on the 11th inst.—Thomas Hodge stated that he saw the accused on the high road at Toton on the day named, with a greyhound. When the latter got near witness he said, " I say, gaffer, I'd like to have a run with my dog," and then went into an adjoining field, started a hare, and set the dog after it.—The bench fined the accused 20s.

shown by the prosecution of George Adcock of Toton in 1862, who was prosecuted for setting a dog to chase a hare and fined 20 shillings.[2]

Gamekeepers patrolled the banks of rivers where they apprehended 2 men catching eels, one of whom was given a custodial sentence (1858). The land therefore provided food, cereals and meat from domesticated animals and wild creatures. The land also provided space for leisure activities such as hawking (17th century) shooting and fishing.

---

[1] Nottingham Evening Post 19th Aug 1885
[2] Nottingham Guardian 28th March 1862

Industry

Man has changed the landscape by straightening rivers, creating weirs, removing trees and bringing pollution. The first industry (recorded in the Domesday Book 1086) was an agricultural one. A water mill necessary to produce flour has been in existence for centuries using the water of the River Erewash. In order to maintain enough power, channels and a weir were created. A mill pond was in existence until the mid 1950s when it was filled in and landscaped, a danger to children but a loss to water loving creatures. The River Erewash was straightened in the 1930s flood prevention scheme.

A bigger danger to the River came from industrial pollution from higher up, from the heavy industry of Stanton iron works, from spillages at Toton Sidings and coal and chemical pollution from further north. Litter has also been a problem (and still is) with shopping trolleys among other things pulled out of the river.

April 1928 saw an investigation into fish deaths (roach, dace and gudgeon) in the River Erewash, which was possibly caused by corrosive acid. In 1943 two tons of dead fish were removed from the Erewash canal, which were thought to have floated down from Sandiacre. The cause of the deaths of the roach was not established. Headlines in 1938 – *Slaughter by Pollution in Trent Board's fishery area. – sufficient noxious matter is being deposited to restrict the fullest reproductive activity among fish - there are many miles of water which neither fish nor insect can survive.* While the Board (River Trent Catchment Board set up in 1931) covered many rivers including the Derwent and Trent, the report states that *"the rivers Churnet and Erewash were barren of fish."*[3] A newspaper article October 1945 notes that the River Erewash was "foul beyond description" and that even the "water rats had fled or been poisoned." It was thought that the cause was oil and coal washing at Pinxton. In 1950 the Trent Fishery Board was set up which reported that the River Erewash was devoid of fish. This Board did note some success in combating pollution in parts of the River Trent but notes there was a long way to go. Improvements in sewage disposal appeared to be an issue. There are seven sewage works along the River Erewash.

River Black Spots

Erewash Charge : Trent Ranks High

SIR PERCIVAL HEYWOOD (chairman) expressed, at a meeting of the Trent Fishery Board at Derby yesterday, alarm at the existence of three black spots in the area from the point of view of pollution. These were the Erewash, Tame and Churnet.

The Board's policy, he said, was always one of peaceful persuasion. It could only institute a prosecution where fish destruction could be proved.

The chairman was replying in particular to a suggestion by Mr. J. J. Smith (Leicester) that drastic action should be taken in connection with the pollution of the Erewash by oil and coal washing at Pinxton. Mr. Smith declared that the river was foul beyond description. Even the water rats had fled or been poisoned and whereas formerly the stream was full of trout, not a worm would live in it now.

MORE INSPECTORS

The railways have also played a part in human and wildlife activity. Toton Sidings which arrived in the mid 19th century expanded to become the largest marshalling yards in Europe. Wagons loaded with coal were brought to the Sidings where coal trains were assembled in order to distribute the fuel around the U.K. Accidents were common. Horse power changed to steam power and finally following the Second World War the engines were converted to diesels. In 1950s tanks, now no longer used for military purposes, scraped away a section of hillside to create more land for Sidings for the shunting of trucks and wagons. Air pollution caused by fumes from steam engines must have affected plant growth. Fog (made worse by engine emissions) was a common weather phenomena in the early 20th century. Diesels brought less air pollution and less industrial accidents. The 1960s saw a decrease in the need for coal and a reduction in the railway system. Much of this land became redundant and was colonised by scrub and birch. This has recently been of benefit to wildlife. Air

---

[3] Derby Daily Telegraph 30th March 1938

pollution now comes from traffic. A sign that air pollution is gradually improving can be seen in the numbers and varieties of mosses and lichens that have been recorded recently. This is an encouraging sign for the future, which should be fostered and embraced.

Housing

Following the First World War and the sale of Toton as a Manor (1921) many houses were built and farms went into decline. The growth of housing was slow in the 1920s and 1930s and residents remember bats in barns, and a plethora of bluebells, and a real leafy country lane (Stapleford Lane). There were various spinneys, formerly the preserve of the chief landowner. The last remaining spinney is at the top of Stapleford Lane adjacent to a once thriving rose growing nursery. The leafy woodland path through the spinney (off what is now Banks Road), where children lugged home logs for bonfire night, has now disappeared in a large housing estate. The wildlife that inhabited the spinney has also vanished except for perhaps a few birds.

Path through the spinney

The 1960s saw the development of the Banks/Bispham Road estate, with houses, schools and many roads. This was followed by another huge expansion of houses in the 1980s with the development of Swiney Way and extension of Banks Road estate. The 1990s saw Grange farm (which had changed from farm to restaurant in 1940s) disappear and the creation of more roads and houses near Toton Corner, covering the land with yet more concrete. This has the hidden effect of not allowing excess

rainwater or floodwater to drain through the underlying gravel and provide water in the water table for the hedges and trees and therefore the creatures that depend on those features. There are now no working farms in Toton.

Toton before Bispham Drive estate. The Spinney centre background

The loss of habitat saw a decline in wildlife. Grey partridge and Red Legged Partridge have disappeared from Toton. Pheasants have been seen by the open land near the tram terminus and in a few gardens. How long will pheasants be seen from the trams when this area also becomes covered over with concrete and bricks?

It is good to see new arrival such as Buzzard and Little Egret. The increase in the Buzzard population shows that small mammals (food source) must be plentiful. It is pleasing to note that this top predator has recovered from the pesticides that killed so many in the latter 20th century. The appearance of the Little Egret is interesting and perhaps a sign of global warming. This is a bird of warmer climes not residing and breeding in the UK until the 1990s. This lovely little heron was first discovered nesting in Nottinghamshire in 2013.

It can be seen that many factors but especially housing in the 20th century have had a profound effect on loss of habitat and therefore loss of species of the natural world of Toton's environs. What changes will there be with the invasion of the area by the High Speed train and yet more houses at the top of Toton's hill?

Wildlife Recordings

Volunteers, both local residents and experts from specialist groups have given their time to record the nature of Toton in the 21st century. Friends of Toton Fields organised several moth evenings, which continued into the early hours, during the summers of 2016 and 2017.

Burnet Moth

Records of insects, birds, mammals, flowers and trees have been noted during the past 10 years – 2008 to 2018. A specialist with specific equipment has visited several times to record bats safely, scientifically, and legally. While every attempt has been made to produce a comprehensive idea of the flora and fauna in Toton there are still many gaps. Fungi have been noted on occasions but not studied in depth. The dragonflies have been recorded although there are probably many more than listed as many of the species in the list were noted when the main focus was insects or even on a daily walk.

Mature tree willow

Ragged Robin

Many species rely on each other. The alder, which likes moist ground especially near rivers, is a pioneer species. The bacterium in the root nodules absorbs nitrogen from the air, which feeds the bacterium and in turn the alder tree improves the fertility of the soil. Alder is also the food plant for the caterpillars of several moths. The catkins provide an early source of nectar and pollen for bees. The seeds are eaten by siskin, redpoll and goldfinch. This is just one example of the relationships in the natural world. We need to be careful when destroying one habitat, as many more creatures may be affected than we first thought.

Dryad's saddle fungus

Cinnabar moth caterpillar

Immature damselfly on grass

Photos by Karen Barker, Gill Morral & Norman Lewis

Toton's Mammals Recorders Marion Bryce (LENS) Adrian Orrell (Bat group) Norman Lewis

Common	Scientific	Location	
Badger	Meles meles		
Bank vole	Myodes glarelus		
Brown hare	Lepus europaeus		
Brown rat	Rattus norvegicus	Toton Fields LNR	
Common shrew	Sorex araneus		
Field vole	Microtis agrestis		
Grey squirrel	Sciurus carolinensis	Toton Fields LNR	
Hedgehog	Erinaceus europaeus	Toton Fields LNR	
House mouse	Mus domesticus	Toton Fields LNR	
Mink	Neovison vison	Toton Sidings South end	
Mole	Talpa europaea	Toton Fields LNR	
Muntjac deer	Muntiacus reevesi		
Otter	Lutra lutra		Visitor from R Trent
Pygmy shrew	Sorex minutus		
Rabbit	Oryctolagus cuniculus	Toton Sidings South end	Toton Sidings South end
Red fox	Vulpes vulpes	Toton Fields LNR	
Stoat	Mustela erminea		
Water shrew	Neomys fodiens	Toton Sidings South end	
Water vole	Arvicola amphibus	Toton Sidings South end	
Weasel	Mustela nivalis	Toton Hill	
Wood mouse	Apodemus sylyvaticus		

Red deer have also been spotted – escapees from Wollaton Park.

Fallow deer have also been spotted, maybe escapes from Wollaton or Risley.

Bats

Common	Scientific	Location
Brown long-eared	Plecotus auritus	Toton Hill
Common Pipistrelle	Pipistrellus pipistrellus	Toton Sidings South end
Daubenton's bat	Myotis daubentonii	Toton Hill
Nathusius' Pipistrelle	Pipistrellus nathusii	Toton Sidings South end
Noctule	Nyctalus noctula	Toton Sidings South end
Soprano Pipistrelle	Pipistrellus pygmaeus	Toton Fields LNR
Whiskered, Brandt's, or Natterer's	Myotis	

Sonogram - calls of Soprano Pipestrelle below left and Noctule below right

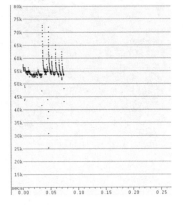 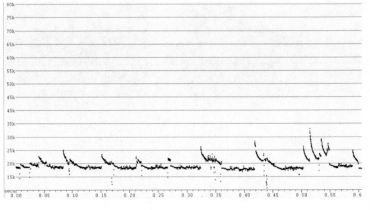

Toton Bats – A. Orrell

Bats (of which there are 1300 species in the world) have lived on earth for 13 million years. They are the only true flying mammals and make up 20% of all mammals in the U.K. Bats belong to the order Chiroptera which is Greek for hand wing; so called because their wings have evolved from fingers elongating with a membrane called a patagium growing between the limbs to form a wing.

There are 18 species of bat in the U.K. of which 17 are breeding. All British bats are microbats, and most are about the size of a thumb and weigh in around 5 grams. Bats can live for up to 30 years although they usually live between 5 to 10 years the oldest recorded bat being a 41 year old Brandts. During the maternity season females gather at their maternity colonies. Bats give birth to one pup per year which weighs approximately a third of its mothers weight, this would be equivalent to a woman giving birth to a baby weighing 16kg (32lb).

Bats have different shaped wings dependant on the habitat they live in, long and narrow for fast straight flight, short and wide for more manoeuvrable flight. Brown long eared bats feed among trees where they glean their food from leaves; they have short broad wings to navigate between trees. Noctules, on the other hand, feed over open fields where they swoop down on their prey and being one of the largest fast flying bats, have long, narrow wings.

Bats are nocturnal and use echolocation to navigate and hunt in the dark. Echolocation is a series of high frequency sounds that bounce back from objects in to the bats large ears. These calls range between 15 and 120khz and the enable the bat to build up a picture of its surroundings and any prey. Pipistrelles feed along the edges and within gaps in the tree canopy hawking insects in flight and can consume up to 3000 insects per night.

Humans can't usually hear the sounds used by bats to echolocate as they are above 18khz. Bats call at different frequencies dependant on species and the habitat used for foraging. Common pipistrelle call at 45khz, whereas soprano pipistrelle call at 55khz. A bat detector can be used which listens for the sounds then outputs the sound in a frequency we can hear. By displaying the frequency at which the bat call we can tell some of the species apart. Daubenton's bat feed just above the water and so have a fast repetition of their call.

Bats can't make their own homes, so instead find cavities in trees and caves, forming clusters to create a stable temperature. Due to the loss of natural roosting places many species now live in man-made structures that offer a stable temperature such as lofts, tunnels, churches, farm buildings and artificial roosts where they group together for warmth. Whilst roosting bats lower their heart rate to reduce the amount of energy they use, a state known as torpor. During the winter months the bats hibernate and lower their body temperature, although unlike other hibernating mammals they have to wake up to drink when the temperature outside increases.

Toton is close to the Erewash river and has areas of small, young woodlands. This means there are few trees with the necessary features to support more than a solitary roosting bat. There are also limited cave like structures, which is where bats can hibernate. There are some tunnels and bridges in the area, that could support small numbers, and daubenton's bats have been seen and heard around these manmade structures.

During Autumn, 2017, bat surveys were carried out in Toton, using an Anabat Express to record bat calls activity in five locations. These recordings were then analysed to see which species of bats had been using the area. The number of species of bats recorded was surprisingly diverse including one of the rarer species, a nathusius pipistrelle. Nathusius pipistrelles are a relatively new species to the county, the first recorded in 2004. They can travel great distances having been found to migrate between England, Holland and Latvia.

Of the twelve species found in Nottinghamshire, seven different species of bat call were recorded in

Toton which included the common pipistrelle, soprano pipistrelle, nathusisus pipistrelle, brown long eared, noctule and members of the myotis family. The myotis family consists of four species in Nottinghamshire, the whiskered, brandts, daubenton and natterer's. It is hard to distinguish the different species through their calls, but we are confident that at least two species of myotis can be found in Toton including the daubenton which has been observed near the River Erewash.

Bat Conservation and Monitoring Due to habitat loss and fragmentation, insecticides, disturbance, lighting and a number of other human activities, bat numbers have declined. Bats are protected by law making it illegal to disturb a bat or its roost unless you have a licence. Throughout the counties bat numbers are monitored and several projects take place. These make sure bat numbers are maintained and also inform on a number of conservation initiatives.

Harp traps (pictured) are used to catch bats to aid conservation; the bats are not harmed and are let go once they have been identified. Projects using trapping can be more targeted towards specific aims and can sometimes lead to tracking the bats using sophisticated equipment.

Bat box checks Bat boxes are put up in several locations and these are checked on an annual basis to ensure numbers aren't decreasing. Static bat call recorders are placed in various locations; these can provide information on bat activity in an area.

Mobile bat call transects are carried out by carrying a mobile detector that can record bat calls, enabling larger areas to be checked for the first time or can be monitored on a yearly basis.

Bat Rescue Both the Notts and Derby groups provide a bat rescue service. Any bat found in distress will be collected, assessed and either released or taken in for treatment until release is possible.

Monitoring equipment

Local organisations Nottinghamshire Bat Group, Derbyshire Bat Conservation Group

Local Birds

This list is written in the order of the Collins bird book. Ainslie Carruthers began recording Toton's birds in 1963. This is a list of species seen in the last 50 years or so. Birds which are listed here as uncommon may be common elsewhere. Bird populations vary for many reasons. Global climate/weather conditions may have influenced the spread of the egret which have now settled in the area and are roosting in our little patch. The reduction in the use of pesticides, such as DDT, has allowed the increase in some birds of prey such as buzzards, which disappeared from our area for a while and have now come back. Other residents have noted the loss of some birds due to habitat loss, for example cuckoos which used to call/sing in the area until the electricity board cut down their favourite tree.

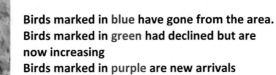

Birds marked in blue have gone from the area.
Birds marked in green had declined but are now increasing
Birds marked in purple are new arrivals

Family	Name	Rarity	Resident/Visitor
Grebes	Great Crested Grebe	Uncommon	Visitor
Cormorants	Cormorant	Fairly Common	Visitor
Herons, storks, ibises	Eurasian Bittern	Very rare	Only seen once in the area
	Little Egret	Common	Visitor
	Grey Heron	Common	Visitor
Swans	Mute Swan	Fairly Common	Visitor - occasionally seen accompanied by cygnets
Geese	Pink-footed Goose	Uncommon	Flying over the Area
Geese	Greylag Goose	Uncommon	Flying over the Area
Geese	Canada Goose	Common	Flying over the Area
Dabbling ducks	Mallard	Fairly Common	Resident
Dabbling ducks	Eurasian Teal	Uncommon	Winter visitor
Diving ducks	Tufted Duck	Uncommon	Winter visitor
Sawbills	Goosander	Uncommon	Winter visitor
Vultures	Osprey	Uncommon	Passage Migrant
Kites & harriers	Red Kite	Uncommon	Flying over the Area
Buzzards	**Buzzard**	Fairly Common	Resident
Hawks	Sparrowhawk	Fairly Common	Resident
Falcons	Kestrel	Uncommon	Resident
	Hobby	Uncommon	Summer Visitor
	Merlin	Uncommon	Winter Visitor
Partridges & Pheasants	**Red-legged Partridge**	Uncommon	Visitor
	Grey Partridge	Uncommon	Visitor
	Common Pheasant	Common	Resident
Rails, crakes & coots	Moorhen	Common	Resident
	Coot	Uncommon	Visitor

Plovers & lapwings	Lapwing	Uncommon	Winter Visitor
Sandpipers, snipes et al	Green Sandpiper	Uncommon	Winter Visitor
	Common Redshank	Uncommon	Winter Visitor
	Woodcock	Uncommon	Winter Visitor
	Common Snipe	Uncommon	Winter Visitor
Gulls	Black-headed Gull	Common	Visitor
	Common Gull	Uncommon	Winter Visitor
	Mediterranean Gull	Uncommon	Winter Visitor
	Herring Gull	Uncommon	Winter Visitor
	Yellow-legged Gull	Uncommon	Winter Visitor
	Lesser Black-backed Gull	Uncommon	Winter Visitor
	Great Black-backed Gull	Uncommon	Winter Visitor
Terns	Common Tern	Uncommon	Summer Visitor
Pigeons & doves	Feral Pigeon	Common	Resident
	Stock Dove	Common	Resident
	Wood Pigeon	Common	Resident
	Collared Dove	Common	Resident
Cuckoos	Cuckoo	Uncommon	Summer Visitor
Owls	Tawny Owl	Uncommon	Resident
	Barn Owl	Uncommon	Resident
	Little Owl	Uncommon	Resident
Swifts	Common Swift	Common	Summer Visitor – overhead
Kingfishers	Kingfisher	Fairly Common	Resident
Woodpeckers	Green Woodpecker	Fairly Common	Resident
	Great Spotted Woodpecker	Fairly Common	Resident
Larks	Sky Lark	Uncommon	Resident
Swallows & martins	Sand Martin	Uncommon	Summer Visitor
	Barn Swallow	Uncommon	Summer Visitor – overhead
	House Martin	Uncommon	Summer Visitor
Pipits & wagtails	**Meadow Pipit**	Uncommon	Visitor
	Pied Wagtail	Uncommon	Resident
	Grey Wagtail	Uncommon	Winter Visitor
Wrens, waxwings et al	Wren	Common	Resident
	Waxwing	Uncommon	Winter Visitor
Accentors	Dunnock	Common	Resident
Thrushes	Robin	Common	Resident
	Common Redstart	Uncommon	Passage Migrant
	Northern Wheatear	Uncommon	Passage Migrant
	Stonechat	Uncommon	Visitor

	Song Thrush	Fairly Common	Resident
	Redwing	Common	Winter Visitor
	Mistle Thrush	Fairly Common	Resident
	Fieldfare	Common	Winter Visitor
	Blackbird	Common	Resident & winter visitor
Warblers	Garden Warbler	Uncommon	Resident
	Blackcap	Common	Resident
	Lesser Whitethroat	Uncommon	Resident
	Common Whitethroat	Common	Resident
	Grasshopper Warbler	Uncommon	Passage Migrant
	Willow Warbler	Common	Summer Visitor
	Chiffchaff	Fairly Common	Resident
	Goldcrest	Uncommon	Resident & winter visitor
Flycatchers	Spotted Flycatcher	Uncommon	Summer Visitor
Tits	Great Tit	Common	Resident
	Coal Tit	Fairly Common	Resident
	Blue Tit	Common	Resident
	Willow Tit	Uncommon	Visitor
	Long-tailed Tit	Common	Resident
Nuthatches	European Nuthatch	Uncommon	Visitor
Crows	Magpie	Common	Resident
	Jay	Uncommon	Resident
	Jackdaw	Common	Flying Over Area
	Rook	Common	Flying Over Area
	Carrion Crow	Common	Resident
	Raven	Uncommon	Visitor
Starlings	Starling	Common	Resident & winter visitor
Sparrows	House Sparrow	Common	Resident
	Tree Sparrow	Uncommon	Resident
Finches	Chaffinch	Common	Resident
	Brambling	Uncommon	Visitor
	Linnet	Common	Resident
	Lesser Redpoll	Uncommon	Winter Visitor
	Goldfinch	Common	Resident
	Greenfinch	Common	Resident
	Siskin	Uncommon	Winter Visitor
	Bullfinch	Fairly Common	Resident
Buntings	**Reed Bunting**	Uncommon	Visitor
	Yellowhammer	Uncommon	Resident

Recorders - Ainslie Carruthers, Marion Bryce, Brian Parkes   Photographs – K Barker

Fish

In 2009 members of Friends of Toton Fields together with the Environment Agency released 500 young grayling into the Erewash at sites near the Greenwood Centre, Carrfield Avenue and further upstream. These fish are related to Salmon. Whilst it has been recorded that Grayling are still present (2017), it is not known if they are breeding here.

chub

Species recorded since 2010 *Local Resident*

The fish listed below were mostly caught using maggots and predominately float fishing. I have however caught chub, barbell, and roach using cubed luncheon meat, either float fishing or ledgering. The perch and pike can be caught on spinners and other lures as well as dead fish. Bread flake, bread paste, cheese casters and trout pellets have also proved successful from time to time. Also when the blackberries are ripe these can be thrown in as loose feed for the chub who appear rather partial to them.

Species	Size between	Weight
Bullhead	2 - 4 inch	
Minnows	2 - 4 inch	
Gudgeon	2 - 4 inch	
Bleak	3 - 6 inch	
Dace		2-12 oz
Roach		1 oz – 1lb 8oz
Rudd		1 oz – 6 oz
Chub		1 oz – 4lb 12oz
Perch		½ oz -2lb
Barbel		1 oz - 4lb
Pike		1lb 8oz upwards
Grayling		3 oz – 12oz
Brown Trout		Ilb 4oz upwards
Ruffe	2 -5 inch	
Bream	3inch upwards	

Butterflies Recorded by Marion Bryce, Brian Parkes & Brian Wetton

Green-veined white

Butterflies are easily observed especially when the sun is shining.
Different habitats have varied species. Mature woodlands often support
Fritillaries while grassland often supports Skipper species, Meadow Browns,
Marbled Whites and Gatekeepers. Brambles are a favoured nectar source for butterflies.

26 species

Scientific name	Common Name	Location
Thymelicus sylvestris	Small Skipper	Toton Sidings Toton Hill Portland Rd meadow
Thymelicus lineola	Essex Skipper	Toton Sidings Portland Rd meadow
Ochlodes sylvanus	Large Skipper	Toton Sidings Toton Hill
Erynnis tages	Dingy Skipper	Toton Sidings
Gonepteryx rhamni	Brimstone	Toton Hill Portland Rd meadow Manor Farm
Pieris brassicae	Large White	Sidings Toton Hill
Pieris rapae	Small White	Sidings Toton Hill Portland Rd meadow Toton Fields
Pieris napi	Green-veined White	Toton Sidings Toton Hill Portland Rd meadow
Anthocharis cardamines	Orange Tip	Sidings Toton Hill Portland Rd meadow Manor Farm
Callophrys rubi	Green Hairstreak	Toton Sidings
Neozephyrus quercus	Purple Hairstreak	Toton Sidings Oak near Erewash bridge 1 male
Lycaena phlaeas	Small Copper(1)	Toton Sidings
Polyommatus icarus	Common Blue	Toton Sidings Toton Hill
Celastrina argiolus	Holly Blue	Portland Rd meadow Toton Fields
Vanessa atalanta	Red Admiral	Toton Sidings Toton Hill Manor Farm
Vanessa	Painted Lady	Garden (2 only)
Aglais urticae	Small Tortoiseshell	Toton Hill Portland Rd meadow Toton Fields
Aglais io	Peacock	Toton Sidings Toton Hill Manor farm
Polygonia c album	Comma	Sidings Toton Hill Portland Rd meadow Manor Farm
Pararge aegeria	Speckled Wood	Sidings Toton Hill Portland Rd meadow Manor Farm
Pyronia tithonus	Gatekeeper	Sidings Toton Hill Portland Rd meadow Manor Farm
Maniola jurtina	Meadow Brown	Sidings Toton Hill Portland Rd meadow
Aphantopus hyperantus	Ringlet	Sidings Toton Hill Portland Rd meadow Manor Farm
Coenonympha pamphilus	Small Heath	Toton Sidings
Melanargaria galathea	Marbled White	Toton Sidings
Plebius agestis	Southern Brown Argus	

Note No Southern Brown Argus seen this year (2017) in Toton.

*Note Toton Fields location = Toton Fields Local Nature Reserve (Toton Fields LNR) Likewise Manor Farm =
Manor Farm Local Nature Reserve (LNR)*

Large Skipper

Marbled White

Ringlet

Moths

Moths come in a huge variety of sizes, colours and shapes but most are rarely seen because they fly at night. A few are active during the day, (for example the Burnet moth) while some can be found resting but the majority are discovered when they are attracted to a light source after dark. With the help of LENS, several moth watching expeditions were made during 2016 and 2017.

On the first occasion 62 moth species were trapped and identified. The most numerous species were the Water Veneer, Smoky Wainscot and Dingy Footman, followed by the Rivulet. The Water Veneer larvae are entirely aquatic, feeding on various aquatic plants such as pondweeds (*Potamogeton*) and Canadian waterweed (*Elodea canadensis*). The Smoky Wainscot lives in rough grassy areas, the larval food plants are mainly grasses. The Rivulet lives in woodland margins, hedgerows and grassy embankments. The Dingy Footman feeds on various lichens. Red Campion (*Silene dioica*) is the preferred food plant for the Rivulet, the caterpillars living inside the seed capsules, eating the seeds.

The moth trapping sessions were planned for different times of the year in order to record a range of species; those that emerge in the Spring and also those that prefer the Summer or Autumn depending on their particular food source. All sessions discovered a variety of species demonstrating that Toton sites are diverse. Many of the species recorded are common moths such as the Heart and Dart, a common species which flies from May to July. The larva feeds on various plants. This was closely followed by another general feeding strategist, the Double Square-spot. The single generation flies in June and July, in wooded habitats. The caterpillars hibernate when quite small and feed in spring on various trees and shrubs.

During the study period (2016/7) there were some less common species found such as Blackneck, White-spotted Pug and Beautiful Hook-tip which have LOCAL status i.e. records are localised or patchy. They have been assigned Nottinghamshire Conservation Grade 2 or 3. On two occasions, a Nationally Scarce birch feeding species – the distinctive yellow Angle-Striped Sallow, was recorded. This species has its stronghold in Nottinghamshire. An Old Lady moth was also recorded. The Old Lady is a huge, sombre-coloured moth. It frequents damp localities as well as waste ground and gardens. The adults are on the wing in July and August. The caterpillars feed in the spring after overwintering, on Blackthorn (*Prunus spinosa*), and other shrubs and trees.

It is thought that given the abundance of trefoils and other legumes in the area surveyed, there should certainly be a chance that some rare moth species such as Chalk Carpet or Annulet could be present. The occurrence of Green Hairstreak, Southern Brown Argus and Dingy Skipper lends strength to this possibility – as the two aforementioned moths often occur together with this suite of butterflies at other UK sites rich in trefoils.

As the flight times of moths can vary from one year to the next, it often takes a number of years of trapping before these species are recorded.

Recorders Dr Sheila Wright Nottinghamshire Larger Moth Recorder,& Curator of Natural Sciences (Biology)Nottingham Natural History Museum at Wollaton Hall, Marion Bryce (LENS- Long Eaton Natural History Society, Brian Parkes (local resident)

Locations surveyed   Greenwood = Greenwood centre, Sidings = Toton Sidings, Hill = Toton Hill

*Order is alphabetical by common name, Species marked * confirmed by dissection ‡ = micro moths,*
Items in bold denote of County Importance

Common Name`	Scientific Name	Location
Angle Shades	Phlogophora meticulosa	Hill
Angle-striped Sallow	Enargia paleacea	Hill
Ash-bark Knot–horn	Euzophera pinguis	Sidings
Barred Yellow	Cidaria fulvata	Sidings south end
Beautiful Hook-tip	Laspeyria flexula	Sidings south end, Greenwood
Bee Moth	Aphomia sociella	Sidings south end
Birch Marble	Apotomis betuletana	Hill
Bird-cherry Ermine	Yponomeuta evonymella	Greenwood
Blackneck	Lygephila pastinum	Sidings south end
Bordered Beauty	Epione repandaria	Sidings
Bordered White	Bupalus piniaria	Greenwood
Bright-line Brown-eye	Lacanobia oleracea	Greenwood
Brimstone Moth	Opisthograptis luteolata	Hill, Greenwood , Sidings south end
Brown House-moth	Hofmannophila pseudospretella	Hill
Brown Rustic	Rusina ferruginea	Sidings
Buff Arches	Habrosyne pyritoides	Greenwood Centre
Burnet Companion	Euclidia glyphica	
Campion	Sideridis rivularis	Greenwood Centre
Canary-shouldered Thorn	Ennomos alniaria	Toton Hill
Centre-barred Sallow	Atethmia centrago	
Chimney Sweeper	Odezia atrata	Sidings
Chinese Character	Cilix glaucata	Toton Hill
Chocolate-tip	Clostera curtula	Greenwood centre
Cinnabar	Tyria jacobaeae	
Clay	Mythimna ferrago	Sidings
Clouded Border	Lomaspilis marginata	Greenwood Centre
Clouded-bordered Brindle	Apamea crenata	Sidings
Clouded Drab	Orthosia incerta	Greenwood Centre
Clouded Silver	Lomographa temerata	Sidings south end & sidings
Codling Moth	Cydia pomonella	Hill, Sidings South end
Common Carpet	Epirrhoe alternata	Sidings south end, Greenwood
Common Emerald	Hemithea aestivaria	Sidings south end
Common Grey	Scoparia ambigualis	Greenwood
Common Marbled Carpet	Dysstroma truncata	Toton Hill
Common/Dark Marbled Carpet agg	Dysstroma truncata/citrata	
Common Plume	Emmelina monodactyla	Toton Hill
Common Quaker	Orthhosia cerasi	Greenwood, Sidings,
Common Rustic	Mesapamea secalis	Toton Hill, Greenwood
Common Swift	Korscheltellus lupulina	Toton Hill
Common Wave	Cabera exanthemata	Sidings
Common Wainscot	Mythimna pallens	Sidings
Common White Wave	Cabera pusaria	Sidings south end, Greenwood
Common Yellow Conch	Agapeta hamana	Greenwood
Copper/Svensson's Copper Underwing	Amphipyra pyramidea	Toton Hill
Copper Underwing agg.	Amphipyra pyramidea agg.	Toton Hill
Coronet	Craniophora ligustri	Greenwood
Dark Arches	Apamea monoglypha	Sidings
Dingy Footman	Eilema griseola	Greenwood
Dot Moth	Melanchra persicariae	Greenwood Centre
Double-square Spot	Xestia triangulum	Sidings south end, Greenwood
Double-striped Pug	Gymnoscelis rufifasciata	Sidings

Drinker	Euthrix potatoria	Greenwood Centre
Dun-bar	Cosmia trapezina	Greenwood
Dusky Thorn	Ennomos fuscantaria	Toton Hill
Dwarf Cream Wave	Idaea fuscovenosa	
Early Thorn	Selenia dentaria	Greenwood
Elbow-stripe Grass-veneer	Agriphila geniculea	Toton Hill
Elder Pearl	Anania coronata	Greenwood
Elephant Hawk-moth	Deilephila elpenor	Sidings south end, Greenwood
Fan-foot	Herminia tarsipennalis	Greenwood Sidings south end
Figure of 80	Tethea ocularis	Sidings
Flame	Axylia putris	Sidings south end, Greenwood
Flame Carpet	Xanthorhoe designata	Sidings
Flame Shoulder	Ochropleura plecta	Hill, Greenwood, Sidings south end
Garden Carpet	Xanthorhoe fluctuata	Greenwood
Garden Grass-veneer	Chrysoteuchia culmella	Toton Sidings
Ghost moth	Hepialus humuli	
Gold Spot	Plusia festucae	Sidings
Grass moths‡	Crambus spp	Toton Sidings
Green Arches	Anaplectoides prasina	Toton Sidings south end
Green Carpet	Colostygia pectinataria	Toton Hill, Greenwood
Green Pug	Pasiphila rectangulata	Greenwood Centre
Grey Pug*	Eupithecia subfuscata	Toton Sidings
Heart & Dart	Agrotis exclamationis	Sidings south end, Greenwood
Hebrew Character	Orthosia gothica	Toton Fields LNR
Herald	Scoliopteryx libatrix	Greenwood
Humming-bird Hawk-moth	Macroglossum stellatarum	
Ingrailed Clay	Diarsia mendica	Greenwood
Iron Prominent	Notodonta dromedarius	Greenwood
July Highflyer	Hydriomena furcata	Greenwood
Knapweed Conch	Agapeta zoegana	Sidings south end
Large fruit-tree tortrix	Archips podana	Sidings
Large Twin-spot carpet	Xanthorhoe quadrifasiata	Toton Sidings
Large Yellow Underwing	Noctua pronuba	Toton Hill
Latticed Heath	Chiasmia clathrata	Toton Sidings
Leopard Moth	Zeuzera pyrina	Toton Sidings south end
Lesser Broad-bordered Yellow Underwing	Noctua janthe	Greenwood Centre
Lesser Yellow Underwing	Noctua comes	Toton Hill, Greenwood
Light Arches	Apamea lithoxylaea	Sidings south end
Light Brown Apple Moth	Epiphyas postvittana	Toton Hill
Light Emerald	Campaea margaritaria	Toton Sidings south end
Little Emerald	Jodis lactearia	Greenwood
Marbled Beauty	Bryophila domestica	Greenwood
Marbled Minor	Oligia strigilis	Greenwood
Marbled White Spot	Deltote pygarga	Toton Sidings south end
Middle-barred Minor	Oligia fasciuncula	Toton Sidings south end
Miller	Acronicta leporina	Sidings
Mint moth‡	Pyrausta aurata/purpuralis	Toton Sidings
Mother of Pearl‡	Pleuroptya ruralis	Toton Hill, Greenwood
Mottled Beauty	Alcis repandata	Greenwood
Mottled Pug	Eupithecia exiguata	Sidings
Mottled Rustic	Caradrina morpheus	Sidings south end
Mouse Moth	Amphipyra tragapoginis	Toton Hill
Notch Wing Tortix	Acleris emargana	Toton Hill
Old Lady	Mormo maura	Greenwood

Pale mottled Willow	Caradrina clavipalpis	Sidings
Pale Straw Pearl	Udea lutealis	Greenwood
Peach Blossom	Thyatira batis	Sidings south end
Pearl Veneer	Agriphila straminella	Sidings
Peppered Moth	Biston betularia	Sidings south end
Poplar Hawkmoth	Laothoe populi	Greenwood
Riband Wave	Idaea aversata	Sidings south end
Rivulet	Perizoma affiniatata	Greenwood
Rosy Minor	Litoligia literosa	Toton Hill
Ruby Tiger	Phragmatobia fuliginosa	Greenwood
Rustic	Hoplodrina blanda	Sidings
Rustic Shoulder-Knot*	Apamea sordens	Toton Sidings
Scalloped Hazel	Odontopera bidentata	Toton Sidings
Scarce Footman	Eilema complana	Sidings
Setaceous Hebrew Character	Xestia c-nigrum	Toton Hill
Shaded Broad-bar	Scotopteryx chenopodiata	Toton Sidings, Greenwood
Short-cloaked Moth	Nola cucullatella	Toton Sidings south end
Shoulder striped Wainscot	Leucania comma	
Shuttle-shaped Dart	Agrotis puta	Toton Sidings south end
Silver-ground Carpet	Xanthorhoe montanata	Toton Sidings south end
Six-spot Burnet	Zygaena filipendulae	Toton Sidings
Silver Y	Autographa gamma	Sidings
Small Blood-vein	Scopula imitaria	Toton Sidings south end
Small Dusty Wave	Idaea seriata	
Small Fan-footed Wave	Idaea biselata	Greenwood
Small Magpie	Anania coronata	Greenwood
Small Phoenix	Ecliptopera silaceata	Toton Sidings
Small Square-spot	Diarsia rubi	Toton Sidings
Smoky Wainscot	Mythimna impura	Toton Hill, Sidings south end
Snout	Hypena proboscidalis	Hill, Greenwood, sidings s end
Spectacle	Abrostola tripartita	Greenwood Centre
Square-spot Rustic	Xestia xanthographa	Toton Hill
Straw Dot	Rivula sericealis	Toton Hill
Straw Grass-veneer	Agriphila straminella	Toton Hill
Sycamore	Acronicta aceris	Greenwood Centre
Tawny Speckled Pug	Eupithecia icterata	Sidings
Toadflax Pug	Eupithecia linariata	Sidings
Treble-bar	Aplocera plagiata	Toton Hill, Greenwood
Treble Lines	Charanyca trigrammica	
Turnip	Agrotis segetum	Toton Sidings
Vapourer	Orgyia antiqua	
Vine's Rustic	Hoplodrina ambigua	Toton Hill
Water Veneer	Acentria ephemerella	Greenwood Centre
White-streak Grass-veneer	Agriphila latistria	Toton Hill
Willow Beauty	Peribatodes rhomboidaria	Toton Hill
White-spotted Pug	Eupithecia tripunctaria	Toton Sidings
Yellow Shell	Camptogramma bilineata	Toton Hill, Greenwood

Recommendations The site should be trapped again, and at different times of year, to see if Chalk Carpet, Annulet or any of the rare Poplar-feeding species such as Hornet Moth (or any other rare species) are present. In addition, the bottom of the cutting holds a great deal of mature broom - this should be surveyed between May and early July for the Broom-tip moth, which we think has been lost from Notts, but may still be hanging on, in as yet undiscovered spots where mature Broom is abundant.   Dr S Wright

Insects, Hoverflies, Dragonflies, Crickets, Bees, Bugs, Beetles

Brian Wetton has observed other species of insect whilst focusing on his main study – Hoverflies. Brian has been studying this species since 1987. In 2011 his attention was drawn to the potential of Toton Sidings and also to the threats to it, both of these warranted him to further his investigations. Since 2011 he has visited the site on nine occasions to survey the insect population. In 2011 visits were made on 9th July, 25th July, and 8th August. Two visits in 2012 on 30th June and 1st September were followed by one visit in 2013 on 14th August. In 2014 there were three further visits on 21st May, 4th July and 11th September. The visits between May and September cover much of the insect flight season but the spring period is under represented and so several early flying insects will have been missed.

The visits followed the unauthorised felling of birch scrub on the site and in 2011 many of the herbaceous plants were able to flower in profusion due to the removal of the birch. Thus the food resources for pollen and nectar feeding insects were at their most profuse. Subsequent re-growth of the birch has reduced these resources in the parts of the site infested by birch and broom. The site however remains a rich patchwork of mixed habitats making it a brownfield site of high biodiversity.

Hoverflies Recorded by Brian Wetton

My special interest has been the hoverfly fauna of the site and in the nine visits I have recorded 52 species. None of the species are classed as nationally "endangered", "vulnerable" or "near threatened" in the recent review of national status. (Ball & Martin 2014) They do however class Meligramma guttatum and Cheilosia mutabilis as national scarce. Moreover Meligramma triangulifera had been previously been categorised as " Nationally Notable". (Falk 1991)

Of the remaining 49 species, four are classed either locally "Rare" or "Scarce" having been recorded in less than 2 or 5 ten kilometre squared in Nottinghamshire respectively. The presence of these together with the overall number of species qualifies the site for designation as a Local Wildlife Site (LWS) (Wetton 2014).

For further information "The Wildlife of Attenborough Nature Reserve" has a section on Hoverflies by Brian Wetton.

Insects, bees, bugs & molluscs Recorded by Marion Bryce LENS 2016-2017

Latin name	Common Name	Location	Species
Melolontha melolontha	Common Cockchafer	Toton Sidings	Insect - beetle
Halyzia sedecimguttata	Orange Ladybird		
Coccinella septempuncta	7 spot Ladybird	Sidings + hill	
Rhagonycha fulva	Common Red Soldier beetle	Toton Sidings	
Oedemera nobilis	Swollen-thighed beetle		
Paracorymbia fulva	Tawny Longhorn beetle		
Bombus (Thoracobombus) pascuorum	Common carder Bee	Toton Sidings	Insect - hymenopteran
Bombus (Pyrobombus) pratorum	Early Bumblebee		
Apis mellifera	Honey Bee		
Bombus (Melanobombus) lapidar	Large Red tailed Bumblebee		
Bombus lucorum/terrestris magnus	White tailed Bumblebee		
Conocephalus fuscus	Long winged Cone-head		Insect - orthopteran
Leptophytes punctatissima	Speckled Bush cricket	Toton Sidings	
Pentatoma rufipes	Forest Bug	Greenwood centre	
Acanthosoma haemorrhoidale	Hawthorn Shieldbug		Insect – true bug
Elasmostethus interstinctus	Birch shield Bug	Toton Hill	
Coreus marginatus	Dock Bug		
Volucella zonaria	Hoverfly	Toton Sidings	
Volucella inanis	Hoverfly		
Arion ater agg/	Chocolate slug	Toton Fields LNR	mollusc
Cornu asperum	Common garden snail		
Panorpa communis	Scorpion fly	Manor Park	
Dorcus parallelipipedus	Lesser staghorn beetle	Garden	

Scorpion fly

Long winged cone head

Lesser Stag Beetle

Paracorymbia fulva

Insects, Hoverflies recorded by Brian Wetton

Species	Name		status
Diptera - flies	Tachinidae	Cistogaster globosa	Locally rare
	Tachinidae	Clindromyia	Locally rare
	soldierflies	Beris chalybata	
	soldierflies	Beris Vallata	
	soldierflies	Chloromyia formosa	
	robberfly	Dioctria baumhaueri	
	Dolychopodidae	Argyra argentella	
	Dolychopodidae	Argyra leucoephala	
	Dolychopodidae	Dolichopus ungalatus	
Heteroptera	Dolycoris baccarum	Hairy shieldbug	
	Polomena prasina	Common Green Shield bug	
Coleoptera	Paracorymbia fulva	Longhorn beetle	Red data book
	Clytus arietus	Wasp beetle	
		22 spot ladybird	
		Harlequin ladybird	
	Cantharis nigrans	Soldier beetle	
	Cantharis rusticia	Soldier beetle	
	Phyllopertha horticola	Garden chafer	
	Oedemera lurida		
Hymenoptera		Sawflies	
	Arge cyanocrocea		
	Arge nigripes		
	Allantus cinctus		
	Dolerus varispinus		
	Macrophya annulata		
	Tenthredo amoena		
	Tenthredo arcuata		
	Tenthredo notha		
		Bees	
	Bombus hypnorum		
	Bombus rupestris		
	Andrena bicolour		
		Cuckoo bee	
	Colletes daviesanus		
	Halictus rubicundus		
	Hylaeus hyalinatus		
	Lassioglossum calceatum		
	Lassioglossum leucopus		
	Lassioglossum morio		
	Lassioglossum smeathmanellus		
	Megachile versicolor		
	Megachile willughbiella		
	Osmia leaiana		
	Osmia rufa		

		Solitary wasps	
	Ammophila sabulosa		
	Ectemnius continuus		
	Ectemnius dives		
	Gorytes quadrifasciatus		
	Nysson trimaculatus		

Hoverflies   52 species

Family/Species	Habitat	Status
Melanostoma mellium	grassland	
Melanostoma scalare	herbage	
Platycheirus albimanus	general	
Platycheirus angustatus	marsh & wet grass	
Platycheirus clypeatus	grassland	
Platycheirus manicatus	general	
Platycheirus scutatus	general	
Paragus haemorrhous	cleared ground	
Chrysotoxum bicinctum	grassland	
Chrysotoxum verralli	waterside	Locally scarce
Epistrophe eligans	scrub	
Epistrophe nitidicollis	scrub & wood	Local
Episyrphus balteatus	general	
Eupeodes corollae	grassland	
Eupeodes luniger	general	
Melangyna compositarum/labiatarum	hogweed	
Meligramma guttatum	wet woodland	Locally Rare Nationally Scarce
Meligaramma triangulifera*	scrub & wood	Locally Rare Nationally Notable
Scaeva pyrastri	gardens, wastelands, grass	Summer migrant
Scaeva selenitica	conifers	Local
Sphaerophoria scripta	grassland	
Syrphus ribesii	general	
Syrphus vitripennis	general	
Xanthogramma pedissequum	grassland	Locally Rare
Cheilosia bergenstammi	herbage	
Cheilosia illustrata	herbage	
Cheilosia latifrons	herbage	Locally Rare
Cheilosia mutabilis	marsh & scrub	Locally Rare Nationally Scarce
Cheilosia pagana	herbage	
Cheilosia proxima	umbels	
Cheilosia scutellata	herbage	
Cheilosia vernalis	herbage	
Riponnensia splendens	herbage	
Eristalinus sepulchralis	marsh & wet grass	
Eristalis arbustorum	general	
Eristalis intricarius	scrub & woods	
Eristalis nemorum	scrub & herbage	
Eristalis pertinax	general	
Eristalis tenax	general	
Helophilus hybridus	marsh & wet grass	

Helophilus pendulus	herbage	
Helophilus trivittatus	thistles & umbels (hogweed)	Local
Myathropa florea	general	
Eumerus funeralis	gardens	Local
Eumerus strigatus	wetland	
Merodon equestris	general	
Heringia heringi	herbage	Locally Scarce
Pipizella viduata	grassland	
Volucella bombylans	scrub & herbage	
Volucella pellucens	scrub & herbage	
Syritta pipiens	general	
Volucella zonaria	*meadows, hedges, verges*	
Volucella inanis	*Toton Sidings urban*	

*Ancient woodland indicator   ‡ italics recorder M Bryce

Many (but not all) of these species can be seen locally at Attenborough Nature Reserve. Some of these can also be seen in gardens like the Lesser bulb fly which likes daffodils Eumerus funeralis and the Onion bulb fly Eumerus funeralis. Many of these hoverflies are striped yellow and black like honey bees and wasps, but some are black (heringia) while others are brown (merodon). Their common denominator is their way of flying – hovering.

Odonata – Dragonflies, damselflies   Recorded by Brian Wetton   *Recorded by K. Barker

Scientific name	Common Name	Flight Period
Aeshna cyanea	Southern hawker	June to October
Aeshna grandis	Brown hawker	July -September
Calopteryx splendens	Banded demoiselle	May- August
Coenagrion puella	Azure damselfly	May- September
Enallagma cyathigerum	Common Blue damselfly	April to September
Ischnura elegans	Blue tailed damselfly	May- September
Sympetrun striolatum	Common Darter	July – October
*Aeshna mixta**	Male migrant hawker	August - October
*Libellula depressa**	Broad Bodied Chaser	May- July

Blue damselfly *Enallagma cyathigerum*   immature

adult

Broad Bodied Chaser

Male migrant hawker *Aeshna mixta*. The long thin triangle on the 1st abdominal segment along with the fact there are two blue spots on each abdominal segment, yellow side bands on the thorax all give clues to the identification.

Flora Recorders Ainslie Carruthers, Norman Lewis & Marion Bryce between 2000 and 2017 & Biological Record Office between 2010 & 2016

Trees and flowers are an important part of the natural world around us. They are the most obvious signs to many folk of the wildlife of an area. Over the centuries plants have been used for their medicinal healing properties (e.g. dock), and their culinary properties (e.g. fennel). The larger trees and shrubs have been used for furniture making or used in housing. The Black Poplar planted alongside the river, is a tree that was once valued because of its special timber characteristics (flexibility and fire resistance).

Key AH = Annual herb, AG = Annual grass, Aq = Aquatic, BH = Biennial herb, B = Biennial, BPH = Bulbous, DT = Deciduous tree, DS = Deciduous shrub, ES = Established shrub, PH = Perennial herb, P = Perennial,   Int = Introduced,   ScP = Scrambling perennial, PI = Post Industrial, Inv = Invasive, ET = Evergreen tree,   DC = Deciduous conifer, RPR = Rare plant register, Alien = Plant not native to Britain,   ARC = Plant species introduced to GB prior to 1492, EN = Endangered, Nat = Native

Botanical (Stace 3)	Common Name	Type	Habitat	Status
Acer campestre	Field Maple	DT	Woods hedgerows	
Acer pseudoplatanus	Sycamore	DT		
Achillea millefolium	Yarrow	PH		
Aegopodium podagraria	Ground-elder	PH	Shady places	
Aesculus hippocastanum	Horse-chestnut	DT	Parks, gardens	
Aethusa cynapium	Fool's Parsley	AH	Arable, waste, lands	
Agrostis capillaris	Common Bent	PG	All areas	
Agrostis gigantea	Black Bent	PG		
Agrostis stolonifera	Creeping Bent	PG	Moist to dry soils	
Aira carophyllea	Silver Hair grass	PI	Grassland	Nat
Aira praecox	Early Hair grass	annual	Grassland	
Alisma plantago-aquatica	Water-plantain	PH	Slow freshwater	
Alliaria petiolata	Garlic Mustard	BH	Shady places	
Allium triquetrum	Three-cornered Garlic	BPH	Waste ground	Int
Allium vineale	Wild Onion	BPH	Dry grassland	Nat
Alnus glutinosa	Alder	DT	Damp or wet areas	
Alopecurus geniculatus	Marsh Foxtail	PG	Mud, wet areas	
Alopecurus pratensis	Meadow Foxtail	PG	Low water meadows	
Anagallis arvensis	Scarlet Pimpernel	AH	Wasteland verges	
Angelica sylvestris	Wild Angelica	PH		
Anisantha sterilis	Barren Brome	AG	Wasteland	
Anthriscus sylvestris	Cow Parsley	PH	All areas	
Apium nodiflorum	Fool's-water-cress	PH	Wet habitats	
Arabidopsis thaliana	Thale Cress	AH	Railway embankment	
Arctium minus	Lesser Burdock	B	Many habitats	
Arenaria serpyllifolia	Thyme-leaved Sandwort	PI	Arable, grassland	Nat
Armoracia rusticana	Horse-radish	PH		Int Es
Arrhenatherum elatius	False Oat-Grass	PG	Verges, grassland	
Artemisia absinthium	Wormwood	PH		
Artemisia vulgaris	Mugwort	PH	Railways wasteland	
Aster novi-beligi	Confused Michael	PI		Int Es

Avena fatua	Wild-oat	AG	Arable, waste land	
Ballota nigra	Black Horehound	PH	Wood edges, banks	
Barbarea vulgaris	Winter-cress	PH		
Bellis perennis	Daisy	PH	Short grass	
Berberis thunbergii	Thunberg's Barberry	shrub		Int
Betula pendula	Silver Birch	DT		
Betula pubescens	Downy Birch	DT		
Bidens tripartita	Trifid Bur-marigold	PH	Wasteland, tracks	
Brassica napus subsp. napus	Rape	AH	Fields, roadsides	
Brassica oleracea	Wild Cabbage	PH	Garden escape waste places	
Brassica rapa subsp	Wild turnip Bargeman's cabbage	BH	Banks canals rivers	
Bromopsis inermis ssp	Hungarian Brome	grass		Int Es
Bromus hordaeaceus ssp	Soft Brome	grass		
Bryonia dioica	White Bryony	ScP	Hedgerows	
Buddleja davidii	Butterfly-bush	Shr	Garden	Int Es
Butomus umbellatus	Flowering-rush	PG	Shallow water/wetland	
Calamagrostis epigejos	Wood Small-reed	PG PI	Grassland	Nat
Callitriche agg.	Water-starwort	Aq		
Caltha palustris	Marsh-marigold	PH	Marshes, ponds	
Calystegia sepium	Hedge Bindweed	ScP	Scrub, fens, hedgerows	Nat
Capsella bursa-pastoris	Shepherd's-purse	AH	Uncultivated land	
Cardamine flexuosa	Wavy Bitter-cress	annual	Shade, moist areas	
Cardamine hirsuta	Hairy Bitter-cress	annual	Rocks walls	
Cardamine pratensis	Cuckoo flower Lady's smock	PH	Damp grassy places	
Carduus crispus	Welted Thistle	BH	Damp grassland	
Carex acuta	Slender Tufted-sedge	sedge	River bank pond edge	
Carex arenaria	Sand Sedge	sedge		
Carex disticha	Brown Sedge	sedge	Marsh, damp places	
Carex flacca	Glaucous Sedge	sedge	Ditches, damp places	Nat
Carex hirta	Hairy Sedge	sedge	Grassland, damp areas	
Carex muricata ssp.pairae	Prickly Sedge	sedge	Grassland	Nat
Carex otrubae	False Fox-sedge	sedge	Pond margins	
Carex ovalis	Oval Sedge	marsh		
Carex pendula	Pendulous Sedge	sedge	Damp woods	Int
Carex remota	Remote Sedge	sedge	Damp woodland	
Carex spicata	Spiked Sedge	sedge	Rough grass, roadside	
Catapodium rigidium	Fern-grass	PI	Grassland	Nat
Centaurea cyanus	Cornflower	AH	Cornfields wasteland	Int
Centaurea nigra	Common Knapweed	PH	Grassland, verges	
Centaurium erythraea	Common Centaury	PH	Dry sandy soil, verges	Nat
Cerastium fontanum	Common Mouse-ear	PH	Waste, walls, verges	
Chaenomeles speciosa	Japanese quince	shrub	Grassy bank by track	
Chaenorhinum minus	Small Toadflax	AH PI	Wasteland rail ballast	
Chamerion angustifolium	Rosebay Willowherb	PH PI		
Chenopodium album	Fat-hen	annual	Disturbed habitat	Nat
Chenopodium bonus-henricus	Good-King-Henry	PH	Bare, grassy places	
Chenopodium rubrum	Red Goosefoot	annual	Arable, wetland	Int
Cichorium intybus	Chicory	PH	Meadows	Int
Circaea lutetiana	Enchanter's-nightshade	PH	Woodland	
Cirsium arvense	Creeping Thistle	PH		
Cirsium palustre	Marsh Thistle	PH	Wet habitats	
Cirsium vulgare	Spear Thistle	PH	Grassland, verges	
Conium maculatum	Hemlock	B	Pastures, waysides	
Conopodium majus	Pignut	PH	Hedgerow/dry grass	

Convolvulus arvensis	Field Bindweed	ScP	Waste/cultivated land	Nat
Conyza canadensis	Canadian Fleabane	AH	Cultivated wasteland	
Conyza sumatrensis	Guernsey fleabane	annual	Woods	Alien
Cornus sanguinea	Dogwood	shrub	Hedgerows wood	Nat
Corylus avellana	Hazel	DS /DT	Scrub, hedgerows	Nat
Cotoneaster conspicus	Tibetan Cotoneaster	shrub		Int
Cotoneaster dielsianus	Diel's Cotoneaster	shrub		Int ES
Cotoneaster francheti	Franchet's Cotoneaster	shrub		Int Es
Cotoneaster horizontalis	Wall Cotoneaster	shrub		Int Es
Cotoneaster lacteus	Late Cotoneaster	shrub		Int ES
Cotoneaster rehderi	Bullate Cotoneaster	shrub		Int Es
Cotoneaster salicifolius	Willow leaved Cotoneaster	shrub		Int Es
Cotoneaster simonsii	Himalayan Cotoneaster	shrub		Int Es
Crataegus laevigata	Midland Hawthorn	Ds/DT	Old woods, hedgerows	
Crataegus monogyna	Hawthorn	DS/DT	Hedge, woodland	
Crepis capillaris	Smooth Hawk's-beard	AH	Rough/waste/grassy	
Crepis vesicaria	Beaked Hawk's-beard	BH	Dry ground, roadsides	
Cynosurus cristatus	Crested Dog's-tail	PH	Meadow, grassland	
Cytisus scoparius	Broom	shrub		Nat
Dactylis glomerata	Cock's-foot	PH	Meadows roadsides	
Daucus carota	Carrot	PH	Calcareous soil	Nat
Deschampsia cespitosa	Tufted Hair-grass	PH	Wet woodland	Nat
Deschampsia flexuosa	Wavy Hair-grass	PG	Grassland wood	Nat
Digitalis purpurea	Foxglove	/PH	Roadside, wood edges	
Dipsacus fullonum	Wild Teasel	BH		
Eleocharis palustris	Common Spike-rush	Sedge	Pond edges	
Elymus caninus	Bearded Couch	PH	Woods, shade	
Elytrigia repens	Common Couch	PH	Wasteland	
Epilobium hirsutum	Great Willowherb	PH	Wasteland, wetland	
Epilobium montanum	Broad-leaved Willowherb	PH		
Equisetum arvense	Field Horsetail	P	Cultivated/waste land	
Equisetum telmateia	Great Horsetail	P	Wet woodlands	
Erigeron acris	Blue Fleabane	PH	Open habitat	Nat
Erodium cicutarium	Common Stork's bill	PI	Arable grassland	Nat
Erophila verna	Common whitlow grass	annual	Meadows, walls, paths	
Euonymus europaeus	Spindle	shrub	Hedgerows, scrub	
Eupatorium cannabinum	Hemp-agrimony	PH	Damp grassland	Nat
Euphorbia helioscopia	Sun Spurge	AH	Waste ground	
Euphorbia peplus	Petty Spurge	AH	Wasteland	
Fallopia baldschuanica	Russian-vine	ScP	Non native	Int ES
Fallopia japonica	Japanese Knotweed	herb		Inv
Festuca brevipila	Hard Fescue	PG		
Festuca rubra	Red Fescue	PH	Dry soils, roadsides	
Ficaria verna	Lesser Celandine	PH	Damp woodland	
Filago minima	Small Cudweed	annual	Heath	
Filago vulgaris RPR	Common Cudweed	annual	Arable grassland PI	Nat
Filipendula ulmaria	Meadowsweet	PH	Wet habitats, ditch	
Foeniculum vulgare	Fennel	PH	Wasteland	Arc
Fragaria vesca	Wild Strawberry	PH PI		Nat
Fraxinus excelsior	Ash	DT	Woodland, hedgerow	
Fumaria officinalis	Common Fumitory	AH	Wasteland	
Galanthus nivalis	Snowdrop	P	Shady places	
Galega officinalis	Goat's-rue	PH	Waste ground	

Galium album	Hedge Bedstraw	PH	Dry habitats	Nat
Galium aparine	Cleavers - goosegrass	AH	Hedges, wasteland	
Galium odoratum	Woodruff	PH	Woodland	
Galium palustre	Marsh-Bedstraw	PH	Wetland habitats	
Galium verum	Lady's Bedstraw	P	Well drained habitats	
Geranium dissectum	Cut-leaved Crane's-bill	AH	Roadside, hedge banks	
Geranium lucidum	Shining Crane's-bill	AH	Dry banks rocky walls	
Geranium molle	Dove's-foot Crane's-bill	AH PI	Open habitat	
Geranium pratense	Meadow Crane's-bill	PH	Farmland grassland	
Geranium pusillum	Small flowered Crane's-bill	PI		Nat
Geranium pyrenaicum	Hedgerow Crane's-bill	PH	Meadows, hedgerows	
Geranium robertianum	Herb-Robert	BH	Woodland, hedgerows	
Geum urbanum	Wood Avens	PH	Hedges, woodland	
Glechoma hederacea	Ground-ivy	PH	Woodland, damp land	
Glyceria fluitans	Floating Sweet-grass	PH	Still/ slow flowing water	
Glyceria maxima	Reed Sweet-grass	PH	Shallow water	
Gnaphalium uliginosum	Marsh Cudweed	annual	Arable PI	Nat
Hedera helix	Common Ivy	ScP	Woodland	
Helminthotheca echioides	Bristly Oxtongue	annual	Rough grass wasteland	
Heracleum sphondylium	Hogweed	PH	Meadow, hedge, wood	
Hieracium sabaudum agg	Autumn Hawkeed	PI	Grassland, woods	Nat
Hieracium salticola	Bluish leaved Hawkweed	P		Int ES
Hieracium umbellatum RPR	Umbellate Hawkweed	PH		
Hieracium vagum	Glabrous headed Hawkweed	PI	Grassland	Nat
Holcus lanatus	Yorkshire-fog	PH PI	Woods	Nat
Hordeum murinum	Wall Barley	AG	Waste ground	
Hordeum secalinum	Meadow Barley	PH	Meadows heavy soil	
Humulus lupulus	Hop	ScP	Damp areas	
Hyacinthoides hispanica	Spanish Bluebell	P		Int
Hyacinthoides non-scripta	Bluebell	P		
Hypericum calycinum	Rose-of-Sharon	shrub		
Hypericum perforatum	Perforate St John's-wort	PH		
Hypericum tetrapterum	Square-stalked St John's-wort	PH	Damp places	
Hypochaeris maculata	Spotted Cat's-ear	P	Calcareous banks	
Hypochaeris radicata	Cat's-ear	PH	Well drained soils	
Ilex aquifolium	Holly	ET	Woodland, hedges	
Impatiens glandulifera	Indian Balsam	A	Wetland	Inv
Inula conyzae	Ploughman's Spikenard	PI	Grassland	Nat
Iris pseudacorus	Yellow Iris	PH	Wet land, ponds	
Juncus articulatus	Jointed Rush	rush	Wet places	
Juncus conglomeratus	Compact Rush	rush	Damp grassland, marsh	
Juncus effusus	Soft Rush	rush	Marsh, ditch, wet area	
Juncus inflexus	Hard Rush	rush	Damp grassland, marsh	
Juncus tenuis	Slender Rush	rush		Int ES
Laburnum x wateri	Laburnum	shrub	Garden escape	Int
Lactuca serriola	Prickly Lettuce	BH	Field crops, orchards	
Lactuca virosa	Great Lettuce	PI	Waste ground	Int
Lamiastrum galeobdolon	Yellow Archangel	PH		
Lamium album	White Dead-nettle	PH	Waste ground	
Lamium purpureum	Red Dead-nettle	PH	Arable, farmland	
Lapsana communis	Nipplewort	AH	Verges, hedgerows	
Larix decidua	European Larch	DC		
Lathyrus latifolius	Broad leaved Everlasting Pea	ScP Pi	Verges, waste land	Int Es
Lathyrus pratensis	Meadow Vetchling	PH	Verges, rough grassland	

Luzula campestris	Field Wood-rush	P	Grassland, woodland	
Lemna minor	Common Duckweed	Aq	Freshwater ponds	Nat
Lemna minuta	Least Duckweed	Aq	Freshwater ponds	Int
Leontodon hispidus	Rough Hawkbit	P	Calcareous grassland	
Lepidium coronopus	Swine Cress	annual	Waste ground	Arc
Leucanthemum vulgare	Oxeye Daisy	PH	Grassland verges	
Ligustrum vulgare	Wild Privet	shrub	Wood edge, hedgerow	
Linaria purpurea	Purple Toadflax	P	Wasteland	Int Es
Linaria repens RPR	Pale Toadflax	PH	Railway banks, ballast	
Linaria vulgaris	Common Toadflax	PH PI	Dry waste ground	Nat
Linaria x sepium RPR	Toadflax hybrid	P	Railway banks wasteland	Nat
Linum catharticum	Fairy Flax	AH PI	Dry grasslands	Nat
Lolium perenne	Perennial Rye-grass	PH	Meadows	
Lonicera japonica	Japanese Honeysuckle	ScP		Int
Lonicera periclymenum	Honeysuckle	ScP	Hedges, woodland	Nat
Lotus corniculatus	Common Bird's foot trefoil	PH PI	Grassland	Nat
Lotus glaber RPR	Narrow-leaved Bird's foot trefoil	P	Railway banks, grassland	
Lotus tenuis RPR	Narrow-leaved Bird's-foot-trefoil	PH		Nat
Lunaria annua	Honesty	BH	Open land	
Lycopus europaeus	Gypsywort	PH	Damp places	
Lysimachia thyrsiflora	Tufted Loosestrife	PH		
Lythrum salicaria	Purple Loosestrife	PH	Wet places	
Malus pumila	Apple	DT		Int
Malva moschata	Musk Mallow	B		Int
Malva sylvestris	Common Mallow	PH	Disturbed ground	
Matricaria recutita	Scented Mayweed	AH	Arable land	
Matricaria discoidea	Pineapple Weed	AH	Cultivated soil	
Meconopsis cambrica	Welsh Poppy	AH	Verges, shady places	
Medicago lupulina	Black Medick	AH	Verges, mown areas	
Medicago sativa subsp. sativa	Lucerne	PH	Field edge, wayside	Int ES
Melilotus albus	White Melilot	AH	Open land, verges	Int ES
Melilotus officinalis	Ribbed Melilot	AH	Railways, verges waste	
Melissa officinalis	Balm	PH		Int ES
Mentha aquatica	Water Mint	PH Aq	Wet meadows, banks	
Moehringia trinervia	Three-nerved Sandwort	AH	Woods shady places	
Myosotis arvensis	Field Forget-me-not	B	Open habitat	
Myosotis scorpioides	Water Forget-me-not	PH	Riverbanks, ponds	
Myosoton aquaticum	Water Chickweed	PH	Ditches, marshes	
Nasturtium officinale agg.	Water-cress	PH		
Odontites vernus	Red Bartsia	annual	Verges wasteland	Nat
Oenothera agg.	Evening Primrose	BH	Open habitats	Int
Oenthera biennis	Common Evening Primrose	Pi B		Int Es
Oenthera cambric	Small Flowered Evening Primrose	Pi B		Int Es
Oenthera glazioviana	Large Flowered Evening Primrose	PI B		Int Es
Oenthera x Britannica	Evening Primrose hybrid	Pi B		Int
Ophrys apifera	Bee Orchid	PH	Well drained	
Origanum vulgare	Wild Marjoram	PH	Grassland	
Papaver dubium	Long-headed Poppy	AH	Roadsides, fields	
Papaver rhoeas	Common Poppy	AH	Disturbed areas, edges	
Papaver somniferum	Opium Poppy	AH	Garden escape	
Parietaria judaica	Pellitory-of-the-Wall	PH	Hedge bank, dry walls	
Pastinaca sativa	Wild Parsnip	B		
Pentaglottis sempervirens	Green Alkanet	PH	Shady places	
Persicaria amphibia	Amphibious Bistort	PH	Wetland, pools	Nat

Persicaria hydropiper	Water-pepper	AH	Damp places	
Persicaria lapathifolia	Pale Persicaria	PH	Waste land arable	Nat
Persicaria maculosa	Redshank	AH	Roadsides, banks	
Phalaris arundinacea	Reed Canary-grass	PH	Wet places	
Phleum pratense	Timothy	PH	Grassland, meadow	
Phragmites australis	Common Reed	grass	Marsh wetland	Nat
Picris hieracoides	Hawkweed Oxtongue	PI	Grassland	Nat
Pilosella aurantiaca	Fox-and-cubs	PH		Int ES
Pilosella officinarum	Mouse-ear-hawkweed	PH PI	Dry grassland	Nat
Pinus sylvestris	Scots Pine	ET		
Plantago lanceolata	Ribwort Plantain	PH	Field edge, tracks	
Plantago major	Greater Plantain	PH	Paths, banks, fields	
Poa angustifolia	Narrow leaved Meadow-grass	PH PI	Grassland	Nat
Poa annua	Annual Meadow-grass	AG	Arable, waste, wayside	
Poa compressa	Flattened Meadow-grass	PH PI	Grassland woods	Nat
Poa pratensis	Smooth Meadow-grass	PH	Verges, paths, meadow	
Poa trivialis	Rough Meadow-grass	PH	Meadow verges woods	
Polygonum arenastrum	Equal-leaved Knotgrass	AH	Arable	Nat
Polygonum aviculare agg.	Knotgrass	AH	Fields, wasteland	
Populus nigra sens. lat.	Poplar	DT	Boggy areas	
Populus nigra subsp. betulifolia	Black Poplar	DT		
Populus tremula	Aspen	PI	Planted, woods	Nat
Populus x canescens	Grey Poplar (P. alba x tremula)	DT	Damp places hedgerow	
Potamogeton pectinatus	Fennel Pondweed	Aq	Ponds, rivers	
Potentilla reptans	Creeping Cinquefoil	PH	Wasteland roadside	
Primula veris	Cowslip	P	Meadows, hedgerows	Nat
Prunella vulgaris	Selfheal	PH	Wood edge, wasteland	
Prunus avium	Wild Cherry	DT		Nat
Prunus domestica	Wild Plum	DT	Wood edge, hedgerow	
Prunus padus RPR	Bird Cherry	DT	Woodland, planted	Nat
Prunus spinosa	Blackthorn - sloe	shrub	Moist well drained soil	Nat
Pyracantha coccinea	Firethorn	shrub		Int Es
Pyrus communis	Pear	DT	Non native	
Quercus cerris	Turkey Oak	DT	Parkland	
Quercus robur	Pedunculate Oak	DT	Hedgerows	
Ranunculus acris	Meadow Buttercup	PH		
Ranunculus aquatilis	Common Water-crowfoot	P Aq	Ponds/ditches	
Ranunculus fluitans	River Water-crowfoot	PH Aq	Rapid flowing water	
Ranunculus repens	Creeping Buttercup	PH		
Ranunculus sceleratus	Celery-leaved Buttercup	PH	Disturbed habitats	
Reseda lutea	Wild Mignonette	Biennial	Grassland, verges	Nat
Reseda luteola	Weld	BH	Roadsides, ballast	
Rhinanthus minor	Yellow-rattle	AH	Grassland	Nat
Ribes rubrum	Red Currant	shrub	Introduced	Nat
Rosa gibbsii	Rose	shrub		
Rosa Hollandica	Dutch Rose	shrub		Int
Rosa rubiginosa agg	Sweet Briar	shrub		Int
Rosa rugosa	Japanese Rose	shrub		Int Es
Rorippa amphibia	Great Yellow-cress	PH		
Rorippa palustris	Marsh Yellow-cress	AH		
Rosa canina	Dog Rose	shrub	Hedgerow, wood edge	
Rubus fruticosus agg.	Bramble	shrub		
Rubus idaeus	Raspberry	Shrub		Nat
Rumex acetosa	Common Sorrel	PH	Grassland wood edge	

Rumex conglomeratus	Clustered Dock	PH	Wasteland	
Rumex crispus	Curled Dock	PH	Cultivated/wasteland	
Rumex hydrolapathum	Water Dock	PH	Canal/pool margins	
Rumex obtusifolius	Broad-leaved Dock	PH	Cultivated/wasteland	
Rumex pulcher	Fiddle Dock	PH	Grassy places	
Rumex sanguineus	Wood Dock	PH	Woods shady places	
Salix acutifolia	Siberian Violet-willow	DS/DT		
Salix alba	White Willow	DT		
Salix aurita	Eared Willow	DS/DT		
Salix caprea	Goat Willow	DS/DT		
Salix cinerea	Grey Willow	DS/DT		
Salix cinerea subsp. oleifolia	Rusty Willow	DS/DT		
Salix daphnoides	Violet Willow	DT	Parks	
Salix purpurea	Purple Willow	DS/DT		
Salix triandra	Almond Willow	DS/DT		
Salix viminalis	Osier	shrub	Wet area by river	Nat
Salix x fragilis	Hybrid Crack-willow	DT		
Salix x holosericea	Hybrid Willow cinerea x vimialis	shrub		Nat
Salix x reichardtii	Hybrid Willow caprea x cinerea	shrub		Nat
Sambucus nigra	Elder	shrub	Woods, hedges	
Sanguisorba officinalis	Great Burnet	PH		
Schedonorus arundinaceus	Tall Fescue	PH	Grassy places	
Schedonorus giganteus	Giant Fescue	PH	Woods	
Schoenoplectus lacustris	Common Club-rush	rush	Still/flowing fresh water	
Scorzoneroides autumnalis	Autumn Hawkbit	PH	Waysides, grassy	
Scrophularia auriculata	Water Figwort	P	Riverbanks, meadows	
Scrophularia nodosa	Common Figwort	PH	Hedges, woodland	
Sedum acre	Biting Stonecrop	PH	Roadsides, wasteland	Nat
Senecio erecifolius	Hoary Ragwort	P PI	Grassland wetland	Nat
Senecio inaequidens	Narrow Leaved Ragwort	PI		Int ES
Senecio jacobaea	Common Ragwort	PH	Pastures , verges	
Senecio viscous	Sticky Groundsel	annual	Wasteland	Int ES
Senecio vulgaris	Groundsel	AH	Open, rough ground	
Silaum silaus	Pepper-saxifrage	PH	Verges, grassland	
Silene coronaria	Rose Campion	PI	Grassland	Int Es
Silene dioica	Red Campion	PH	Woods	
Silene latifolia	White Campion	PH	Fields, hedgerows	
Silene vulgaris	Bladder Campion	PH PI	Pastures wasteland	Nat
Sinapis arvensis	Charlock	AH	Roadsides, railways	
Sisymbrium officinale	Hedge Mustard	BH	Disturbed ground	
Solanum dulcamara	Bittersweet – woody nightshade	ScP		
Solanum lycopersicum	Tomato	Annual	Casual	Int
Solanum nigrum	Black Nightshade	AH	Wasteland	
Solidago canadensis	Canadian Goldenrod	PH	Waysides, scrub	Int ES
Sonchus arvensis	Perennial Sow-thistle	P		Nat
Sonchus asper	Prickly Sow-thistle	AH	Roadsides, wasteland	
Sonchus oleraceus	Smooth Sow-thistle	AH	Bare wasteland	
Sorbus aria agg RPR	Whitebeam	DT	Introduced	Nat
Sorbus aucuparia	Rowan	DT	Planted	Nat
Sorbus intermedia	Swedish Whitebeam	DT		Int ES
Sparganium emersum	Unbranched Bur-reed	PH	Wetland	Nat
Sparganium erectum	Branched Bur-reed	PH	Pond/ditch/ river margins	Nat
Stachys palustris	Marsh Woundwort	PH		

Stachys sylvatica	Hedge Woundwort	PH		
Stellaria graminea	Lesser Stitchwort	PH	Grassland, woodland	
Stellaria media	Common Chickweed	AH	Verges, gardens, waste	
Stellaria neglecta	Greater Chickweed	AH	Damp woods, hedges	
Symphoricarpos albus	Snowberry	DS	Hedges	
Symphytum officinale	Common Comfrey	PH	Damp land, wasteland	
Symphytum x uplandicum	Russian Comfrey (S. asperum x officinale)	PH	Roadsides wasteland	
Tamus communis	Black Bryony	ScP	Woods, hedgerows	Nat
Tanacetum parthenium	Feverfew	herb	Hedgerow	
Tanacetum vulgare	Tansy	PH	Wasteland, roadside	
Taraxacum agg.	Dandelion	PH	Fields, waste places	
Teucrium scorodonia	Wood Sage	PH	Woodland	Nat
Thlaspi arvense	Field Penny-cress	AH	Arable, disturbed area	
Torilis japonica	Upright Hedge-parsley	AH	Dry habitats	Nat
Tragopogon pratensis	Goat's-beard	PH	Railway banks, wayside	
Trifolium arvense	Hare's-foot Clover	AH Pl	Grassland	Nat
Trifolium campestre	Hop Trefoil	AH	Rough grassland verges	
Trifolium dubium	Lesser Trefoil	PH	Wasteland	
Trifolium medium	Zigzag Clover	PH	Grassland	
Trifolium pratense	Red Clover	PH	Pastures	
Trifolium repens	White Clover	PH	Roadside, pastures	
Tripleurospermum inodorum	Scentless Mayweed	annual	Wasteland	Nat
Trisetum flavescens	Yellow Oat-grass	PH	Grassy verges	
Tussilago farfara	Coltsfoot	PH	Hedge banks, arable,	
Typha angustifolia	Lesser Bulrush	PH		
Typha latifolia	Bulrush - reedmace	PH	Emergent plant shallow water	
Ulex europaeus	Gorse	shrub	Grasslands, banks	Nat
Urtica dioica	Common Nettle	PH	Damp disturbed land	
Valerianella locusta	Common cornsalad	annual	Wasteland	Nat
Verbascum lychnitis RPR	White Mullein	BH	Railway banks, verges	Int Es
Verbascum thapsus	Great Mullein	BH	Railway banks, verges	Nat
Veronica chamaedrys	Germander Speedwell	PH	Hedgerows, grassy verges	
Veronica persica	Common Field-speedwell	AH		
Viburnum lantana	Wayfaring-tree	DS/DT		
Viburnum opulus	Guelder-rose	shrub	Woods, hedges	
Vicia cracca	Tufted Vetch	PH	Grassland roadsides	Nat
Vicia hirsuta	Hairy Tare	AH	Rough grassland verges	Nat
Vicia sativa	Common Vetch	AH		
Vicia sepium	Bush Vetch	PH	Banks waste ground	
Vinca major	Greater Periwinkle	PH		
Viola arvensis	Field Pansy	AH	Wasteland verges	Arc
Viola odorata	Sweet Violet	PH	Roadsides	Nat
Viola riviniana	Common Dog-violet	PH	Wood margins	
Vulpia bromoides	Squirrel-tail Fescue	AG	Dry banks	
Vulpia myuros	Rat's-tail Fescue	AG	Cultivated, sandy land	
Ferns				
Dryopteris dilatata	Broad Buckler			
Dryopteris filix-mas	Common Male fern			
Athyrium felix femina	Lady fern			
Pteridium aquilinum	Bracken			
Aspenium scolopendrium	Harts Tongue			
Polypodium vulgare	Common polypody			

Primula Vulgaris - Cowslip

Hogweed

Kidney Vetch

Ragged Robin

Sweet Violet

Sweet Briar

Field Wood-rush, Hoary Plantain

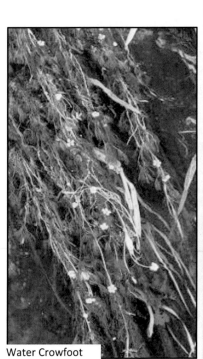

Water Crowfoot

Common Whitlow

Ribwort Plantain

81

Flora in Common Name Order

Some plants like the Bird Cherry and Common Cudweed are listed on the Rare Plant Register - RPR

Common Name	Botanical Order	Common Bird's foot trefoil	Lotus corniculatus
Alder	Alnus glutinosa	Common Centaury	Centaurium erythraea
Almond Willow	Salix triandra	Common Chickweed	Stellaria media
Amphibious Bistort	Persicaria amphibia	Common Club-rush	Schoenoplectus lacustris
Annual Meadow-grass	Poa annua	Common Comfrey	Symphytum officinale
Apple	Malus pumila	Common cornsalad	Valerianella locusta
Ash	Fraxinus excelsior	Common Couch	Elytrigia repens
Aspen	Populus tremula	Common Cudweed	Filago vulgaris RPR
Autumn Hawkbit	Scorzoneroides autumnalis	Common Dog-violet	Viola riviniana
Autumn Hawkweed	Hieracium sabaudum agg	Common Duckweed	Lemna minor
Balm	Melissa officinalis	Common Evening Primrose	Oenthera biennis
Barren Brome	Anisantha sterilis	Common Field-speedwell	Veronica persica
Beaked Hawk's-beard	Crepis vesicaria	Common Figwort	Scrophularia nodosa
Bearded Couch	Elymus caninus	Common Fumitory	Fumaria officinalis
Bee Orchid	Ophrys apifera	Common Ivy	Hedera helix
Bird cherry	Prunus padus RPR	Common Knapweed	Centaurea nigra
Biting Stonecrop	Sedum acre	Common Mallow	Malva sylvestris
Bittersweet	Solanum dulcamara	Common Mouse-ear	Cerastium fontanum
Black Bent	Agrostis gigantean	Common Nettle	Urtica dioica
Black Bryony	Tamus communis	Common Poppy	Papaver rhoeas
Black Horehound	Ballota nigra	Common Ragwort	Senecio jacobaea
Black Medick	Medicago lupulina	Common Reed	Phragmites australis
Black Nightshade	Solanum nigrum	Common Sorrel	Rumex acetosa
Black Poplar	Populus nigra	Common Spike-rush	Eleocharis palustris
Blackthorn - sloe	Prunus spinosa	Common Stork's bill	Erodium cicutarium
Bladder Campion	Silene vulgaris	Common Toadflax	Linaria vulgaris
Blue Fleabane	Erigeron acris	Common Vetch	Vicia sativa
Bluebell	Hyacinthoides non-scripta	Common Water-crowfoot	Ranunculus aquatilis
Bluish leaved Hawkweed	Hieracium salticola	Common Whitlow	Erophila verna
Bramble	Rubus fruticosus agg.	Compact Rush	Juncus conglomeratus
Branched Bur-reed	Sparganium erectum	Confused Michael	Aster novi-beligi
Bristly Oxtongue	Helminthotheca echioides	Cornflower	Centaurea cyanus
Broad leaved everlasting pea	Lathyrus latifolius	Cow Parsley	Anthriscus sylvestris
Broad-leaved Dock	Rumex obtusifolius	Cowslip	Primula Veris
Broad-leaved Willowherb	Epilobium montanum	Creeping Cinquefoil	Potentilla reptans
Broom	Cytisus scoparius	Creeping Thistle	Cirsium arvense
Brown Sedge	Carex disticha	Crested Dog's-tail	Cynosurus cristatus
Bullate Cotoneaster	Cotoneaster rehderi	Cuckoo flower Lady's smock	Cardamine pratensis
Bulrush - reedmace	Typha latifolia	Curled Dock	Rumex crispus
Bush Vetch	Vicia sepium	Cut-leaved Crane's-bill	Geranium dissectum
Butterfly-bush	Buddleja davidii	Daisy	Bellis perennis
Canadian Fleabane	Conyza canadensis	Dandelion	Taraxacum agg.
Canadian Goldenrod	Solidago Canadensis	Diel's Cotoneaster	Cotoneaster dielsianus
Carrot	Daucus carota	Dog rose	Rosa canina agg
Cat's-ear	Hypochaeris radicata	Dog-rose	Rosa canina
Celery-leaved Buttercup	Ranunculus sceleratus	Dogwood	Cornus sanguinea
Charlock	Sinapis arvensis	Dove's-foot Crane's-bill	Geranium molle
Chicory	Cichorium intybus	Downy Birch	Betula pubescens
Cleavers - goosegrass	Galium aparine	Dutch Rose	Rosa Hollandica
Clustered Dock	Rumex conglomeratus	Eared Willow	Salix aurita
Cock's-foot grass	Dactylis glomerata	Early Hair grass	Aira praecox
Cleavers - goosegrass	Galium aparine	Elder	Sambucus nigra
Clustered Dock	Rumex conglomeratus	Enchanter's-nightshade	Circaea lutetiana
Cock's-foot	Dactylis glomerata	Equal-leaved Knotgrass	Polygonum arenastrum
Colt's-foot	Tussilago farfara	European Larch	Larix decidua
Common Bent grass	Agrostis capillaris	Evening Primrose hybrid	Oenthera x Britannica

Fairy Flax	Linum catharticum	Hawthorn	Crataegus monogyna
False Fox-sedge	Carex otrubae	Hazel	Corylus avellana
False Oat-Grass	Arrhenatherum elatius	Hedge Bedstraw	Galium album
Fat-hen	Chenopodium album	Hedge Bindweed	Calystegia sepium
Fennel	Foeniculum vulgare	Hedge Bindweed	Calystegia sepium
Fennel Pondweed	Potamogeton pectinatus	Hedge Mustard	Sisymbrium officinale
Fern-grass	Catapodium rigidium	Hedge Woundwort	Stachys sylvatica
Feverfew	Tanacetum parthenium	Hedgerow Crane's-bill	Geranium pyrenaicum
Fiddle Dock	Rumex pulcher	Hemlock	Conium maculatum
Field Bindweed	Convolvulus arvensis	Hemp-agrimony	Eupatorium cannabinum
Field Forget-me-not	Myosotis arvensis	Herb-Robert	Geranium robertianum
Field Horsetail	Equisetum arvense	Himalayan Cotoneaster	Cotoneaster simonsii
Field Maple	Acer campestre	Hoary Ragwort	Senecio erecifolius
Field Pansy	Viola arvensis	Hogweed	Heracleum sphondylium
Field Penny-cress	Thlaspi arvense	Holly	Ilex aquifolium
Field Wood Rush	Luzula campestris	Honesty	Lunaria annua
Firethorn	Pyracantha coccinea	Honeysuckle	Lonicera periclymenum
Flattened meadow grass	Poa compressa	Hop	Humulus lupulus
Floating Sweet-grass	Glyceria fluitans	Hop Trefoil	Trifolium campestre
Flowering-rush	Butomus umbellatus	Horse-chestnut	Aesculus hippocastanum
Fool's Parsley	Aethusa cynapium	Horse-radish	Armoracia rusticana
Fool's-water-cress	Apium nodiflorum	Hungarian Brome	Bromopsis inermiss ssp
Fox-and-cubs	Pilosella aurantiaca	Hybrid Crack-willow	Salix x fragilis
Foxglove	Digitalis purpurea	Hybrid will caprea x cinerea	Salix x reichardtii
Franchet's Cotoneaster	Cotoneaster francheti	Hybrid willow	Salix x holosericea
Garlic Mustard	Alliaria petiolata	Indian Balsam	Impatiens glandulifera
Germander Speedwell	Veronica chamaedrys	Japanese Honeysuckle	Lonicera japonica
Giant Fescue	Schedonorus giganteus	Japanese Knotweed	Fallopia japonica
Glabrous headed Hawkweed	Hieracium vagum	Japanese Quince	Chaenomeles speciosa
Glaucous Sedge	Carex flacca	Japanese Rose	Rosa rugosa
Goat Willow	Salix caprea	Jointed Rush	Juncus articulatus
Goat's-beard	Tragopogon pratensis	Knotgrass	Polygonum aviculare agg.
Goat's-rue	Galega officinalis	Laburnum	Laburnum x wateri
Good-King-Henry	Chenopodium bonus-henricus	Lady's Bedstraw	Galium verum
Gorse	Ulex europaeus	Lge flowered evening primrose	Oenthera glazioviana
Great Burnet	Sanguisorba officinalis	Late Cotoneaster	Cotoneaster lacteus
Great Horsetail	Equisetum telmateia	Least Duckweed	Lemna minuta
Great Lettuce	Lactuca virosa	Lesser Bulrush	Typha angustifolia
Great Mullein	Verbascum thapsus	Lesser Burdock	Arctium minus
Great Willowherb	Epilobium hirsutum	Lesser Celandine	Ficaria verna
Great Yellow-cress	Rorippa amphibia	Lesser Stitchwort	Stellaria graminea
Greater Chickweed	Stellaria neglecta	Lesser Trefoil	Trifolium dubium
Greater Periwinkle	Vinca major	Long-headed Poppy	Papaver dubium
Greater Plantain	Plantago major	Lucerne	Medicago sativa
Green Alkanet	Pentaglottis sempervirens	Marsh Cudweed	Gnaphalium uliginosum
Grey Poplar	Populus x canescens	Marsh Foxtail	Alopecurus geniculatus
Grey Willow	Salix cinerea	Marsh Thistle	Cirsium palustre
Ground-elder	Aegopodium podagraria	Marsh Woundwort	Stachys palustris
Ground-ivy	Glechoma hederacea	Marsh Yellow-cress	Rorippa palustris
Groundsel	Senecio vulgaris	Marsh-bedstraw	Galium palustre
Guelder-rose	Viburnum opulus	Marsh-marigold	Caltha palustris
Guernsey fleabane	Conyza sumatrensis	Meadow Barley	Hordeum secalinum
Gypsywort	Lycopus europaeus	Meadow Buttercup	Ranunculus acris
Hairy Bitter-cress	Cardamine hirsuta	Meadow Crane's-bill	Geranium pratense
Hairy Sedge	Carex hirta	Meadow Foxtail	Alopecurus pratensis
Hairy Tare	Vicia hirsuta	Meadow Vetchling	Lathyrus pratensis
Hard Fescue	Festuca brevipila	Meadowsweet	Filipendula ulmaria
Hard Rush	Juncus inflexus	Midland Hawthorn	Crataegus laevigata
Evening Primrose	Oenothera agg.	Mouse-ear-Hawkweed	Pilosella officinarum
Hare's-foot Clover	Trifolium arvense	Hawkweed Oxtongue	Picris hieracoides

Mugwort	Artemisia vulgaris	Scarlet Pimpernel	Anagallis arvensis
Musk mallow	Malva moschata	Scented Mayweed	Matricaria chamomilla
Narrow leaved meadow grass	Poa angustifolia	Scentless Mayweed	Tripleurospermum inodorum
Narrow leaved Birds foot Trefoil	Lotus glaber RPR	Scots Pine	Pinus sylvestris
Narrow leaved ragwort	Senecia inaequidens	Selfheal	Prunella vulgaris
Narrow-leaf Bird's-foot-trefoil	Lotus tenuis RPR	Shepherd's-purse	Capsella bursa-pastoris
Nipplewort	Lapsana communis	Shining Crane's-bill	Geranium lucidum
Opium Poppy	Papaver somniferum	Siberian Violet-willow	Salix acutifolia
Osier	Salix viminalis	Silver Birch	Betula pendula
Oval Sedge	Carex ovalis	Silver Hair-grass	Aira carophyllea
Oxeye Daisy	Leucanthemum vulgare	Slender Rush	Juncus tenuis
Pale Persicaria	Persicaria lapathifolia	Slender Tufted-sedge	Carex acuta
Pale Toadflax	Linaria repens RPR	Small Cudweed	Filago minima
Pear	Pyrus communis	Small flowered Cranesbill	Geranium pusillum
Pedunculate Oak	Quercus robur	Small flowered evening primrose	Oenthera cambric
Pellitory-of-the-Wall	Parietaria judaica	Small Toadflax	Chaenorhinum minus
Pendulous Sedge	Carex pendula	Smooth Hawk's-beard	Crepis capillaris
Pepper-saxifrage	Silaum silaus	Smooth Meadow-grass	Poa pratensis
Perennial Rye-grass	Lolium perenne	Smooth Sow-thistle	Sonchus oleraceus
Perennial sow thistle	Sonchuc arvensis	Snowberry	Symphoricarpos albus
Perforate St John's-wort	Hypericum perforatum	Snowdrop	Galanthus nivalis
Petty Spurge	Euphorbia peplus	Soft brome	Bromus hordaeaceus ssp
Pignut	Conopodium majus	Soft-rush	Juncus effusus
Pineapple Weed	Matricaria discoidea	Spanish Bluebell	Hyacinthoides hispanica
Ploughman's spikenard	Inula conyzae	Spear Thistle	Cirsium vulgare
Poplar	Populus nigra sens. lat.	Spiked Sedge	Carex spicata
Prickly Lettuce	Lactuca serriola	Spindle	Euonymus europaeus
Prickly Sedge	Carex muricata ssp.pairae	Spotted Cat's-ear	Hypochaeris maculata
Prickly Sow-thistle	Sonchus asper	Square-stalked St John's-wort	Hypericum tetrapterum
Purple Toadflax	Linaria purpurea	Squirrel-tail Fescue	Vulpia bromoides
Purple Willow	Salix purpurea	Sticky Groundsel	Senecio viscous
Purple-loosestrife	Lythrum salicaria	Sun Spurge	Euphorbia helioscopia
Rape	Brassica napus subsp. napus	Swedish Whitebeam	Sorbus intermedia
Raspberry	Rubus idaeus	Sweet Briar hybrid	Rosa rubiginosa agg
Rat's-tail Fescue	Vulpia myuros	Sweet Briar	Rosa rubiginosa
Red Bartsia	Odontites vernus	Sweet Violet	Viola odorata
Red Campion	Silene dioica	Swine Cress	Lepidium coronopus
Red Clover	Trifolium pratense	Sycamore	Acer pseudoplatanus
Redcurrant	Ribes rubrum	Tall Fescue	Schedonorus arundinaceus
Red Dead-nettle	Lamium purpureum	Tansy	Tanacetum vulgare
Red Fescue	Festuca rubra	Thale Cress	Arabidopsis thaliana
Red Goosefoot	Chenopodium rubrum	Three-cornered Garlic	Allium triquetrum
Redshank	Persicaria maculosa	Three-nerved Sandwort	Moehringia trinervia
Reed Canary-grass	Phalaris arundinacea	Thunberg's Barberry	Berberis thunbergii
Reed Sweet-grass	Glyceria maxima	Thyme-leaved Sandwort	Arenaria serpyllifolia
Remote Sedge	Carex remota	Tibetan Cotoneaster	Cotoneaster conspicus
Ribbed Melilot	Melilotus officinalis	Timothy	Phleum pratense
Ribwort Plantain	Plantago lanceolata	Toadflax hybrid	Linaria x sepium RPR
River Water-crowfoot	Ranunculus fluitans	Tomato	Solanum lycopersicum
Rose	Rosa gibbsii	Trifid Bur-marigold	Bidens tripartita
Rose Campion	Silene coronaria	Tufted Hair-grass	Deschampsia cespitosa
Rosebay Willowherb	Chamerion angustifolium	Tufted Loosestrife	Lysimachia thyrsiflora
Rose-of-Sharon	Hypericum calycinum	Tufted Vetch	Vicia cracca
Rough Hawkbit	Leontodon hispidus	Turkey Oak	Quercus cerris
Rough Meadow-grass	Poa trivialis	Umbellate Hawkweed	Hieracium umbellatum RPR
Rowan	Sorbus aucuparia	Unbranched Bur-reed	Sparganium emersum
Russian Comfrey	Symphytum x uplandicum	Upright Hedge-parsley	Torilis japonica
Russian-vine	Fallopia baldschuanica	Wall Barley	Hordeum murinum
Sand Sedge	Carex arenaria	Rusty Willow	Salix cinerea subsp. oleifolia

Wall Cotoneaster	Cotoneaster horizontalis	Wild Parsnip	Pastinaca sativa
Water Chickweed	Myosoton aquaticum	Wild Plum	Prunus domestica
Water Dock	Rumex hydrolapathum	Wild Privet	Ligustrum vulgare
Water Figwort	Scrophularia auriculata	Wild Strawberry	Fragaria vesca
Water Forget-me-not	Myosotis scorpioides	Wild Teasel	Dipsacus fullonum
Water Mint	Mentha aquatica	Wild Turnip Bargeman's cabbage	Brassica rapa subsp
Water-cress	Nasturtium officinale agg.	Wild-oat	Avena fatua
Water-pepper	Persicaria hydropiper	Willow leaved conoeaster	Cotoneaster salifolius
Water-plantain	Alisma plantago-aquatica	Winter-cress	Barbarea vulgaris
Water-starwort	Callitriche agg.	Wood Avens	Geum urbanum
Wavy Bitter-cress	Cardamine flexuosa	Wood Dock	Rumex sanguineus
Wavy Hairpgrass	Deschampsia flexuosa	Wood Sage	Teucrium scorodonia
Wayfaring-tree	Viburnum lantana	Wood Small-reed	Calamagrostis epigejos
Weld	Reseda luteola	Woodruff	Galium odoratum
Welsh Poppy	Meconopsis cambrica	Wormwood	Artemisia absinthium
Welted Thistle	Carduus crispus	Yarrow	Achillea millefolium
White Bryony	Bryonia dioica	Yellow Archangel	Lamiastrum galeobdolon
White Campion	Silene latifolia	Yellow Iris	Iris pseudacorus
White Clover	Trifolium repens	Yellow Oat-grass	Trisetum flavescens
White Dead-nettle	Lamium album	Yellow-rattle	Rhinanthus minor
White Melilot	Melilotus albus	Yorkshire-fog	Holcus lanatus
White Mullein	Verbascum lychnitis RPR	Wall Barley	Hordeum murinum
White Willow	Salix alba		
Whitebeam	Sorbus aria agg RPR	**Ferns**	
Wild Angelica	Angelica sylvestris	Broad Buckler	Dryopteris dilatata
Wild Cabbage	Brassica oleracea	Common Male fern	Dryopteris filix-mas
Wild Cherry	Prunus avium	Lady fern	Athyrium felix femina
Wild Marjoram	Origanum vulgare	Bracken	Pteridium aquilinum
Wild Mignonette	Reseda lutea	Harts Tongue	Aspenium scolopendrium
Wild Onion	Allium vineale	Common polypody	Polypodium vulgare

Trees in Compartment A Sports Field margins

Native Black Poplar

Salix Daphnoides

The Bryophytes of Toton Sidings   Margaret Crittenden

Introducing the bryophytes

Bryophytes are small green photosynthetic plants that do not produce flowers, seeds or fruits. They include mosses, liverworts and hornworts. They can be small and overlooked and often regarded with at best indifference and at worst antipathy. The closer you look, however, especially if you have a hand lens, the more interesting and complex they appear. Their beauty can only be described as astounding. Most bryophytes inhabit damp or humid places, but they are found all over the world, including mountains and deserts. Some mosses can grow in areas with little water because they can dry out without dying and then 'come back to life' in just seconds when it rains. Bryophytes lack the complex tissues found in flowering plants which makes their cellular structure comparatively simple and restricts their size to a few centimetres at most.

Bryophytes reproduce sexually by producing sperm and eggs but water is required as the sperm need to swim to the eggs to fertilise them. After fertilisation, the egg grows into a stalk (the seta) with a capsule (the sporangium) in which the spores develop and are stored. When ripe, the spores are dispersed from the capsules and rely on wind and water to be carried away so that a new bryophyte plant can grow. Mosses, like other plants, can also reproduce asexually. A small piece of a moss plant can separate and grow into a new plant, or new plants can branch off from old ones. Asexual reproduction allows plants to spread more easily than sexual reproduction.

Bryophytes are thought to be the nearest living relatives to the earliest land plants. They are an immensely important part of the habitats in which they are found, being pivotal in processes such as soil formation and the cycling of water and nutrients. In northern latitudes in particular, their role in bogs in locking up carbon dioxide helps to mitigate the effects of global climate change. They are very sensitive to changes in their habitats and as such are good indicators of environmental change.

We have the richest bryophyte flora in the whole of Europe, particularly in the west of Britain, with more than 1000 native species currently known. Fifty-nine new species have been discovered in the last 20 years.

The bryophytes of Toton Sidings

Scanning the scene at **Toton Sidings** you can see that these tiny plants are everywhere, on trees, stones and covering the ground. Without them, the grasslands, woods and pond margins would not be as green nor as soft on the eye. **Nottinghamshire has an interesting array** of these plants as we

have both lowland heathland and limestone grassland but also because of its large brownfield sites, that often have a much greater selection of habitat types than semi-natural sites. **Toton Sidings** is a case in point, with a mixture of habitats due to the granite and limestone used for ballast for track laying along with concrete posts and various spillages.

Toton Sidings harbours a variety of mosses and liverworts which either 'prefer' acidic or basic (alkaline) places to live. **Forty-seven species** have been found so far and I would expect there to be many more.

The epiphyte **Cryphea heteromalla** *Lateral Cryphaea was found on the bark of oak and willow trees. It creeps along the bark then rears up to produce capsules.*

The moss *Cryphaea heteromalla* and the liverwort *Frullania dilatata,* have spread from relatively unpolluted areas and now occur throughout Britain and Ireland including at Toton Sidings where they grow on the surface of tree bark (epiphytes).

Species of *Orthotrichum* which have crisped leaves when dry may also be spotted. The species found at Toton were mainly *Orthotrichum diaphanum* (White-tipped Bristle-moss) and *Orthotrichum affine* (Wood Bristle-moss) that, even when air pollution was at its worst, managed to survive in urban environments. The presence of the diminutive *Orthotrichum pulchellum* (Elegant Bristle-moss) shows that air quality is improving.

*The liverwort **Frullania dilitata**, Dilated Scalewort (with **Orthotrichum affine** in the centre and top left) found on bark at Toton Sidings.*

The many tracks and paths at Toton Sidings have their own small communities of mosses in less trampled areas and includes *Barbula unguiculata* (Bird's-claw Beard-moss).

*Old Elders are particularly good habitats for **Orthotrichum** species. It looks as if it is covered in pom-poms.*

Barbula unguiculata,
*Bird's-claw Beard-moss.
Each plant is about 4mm*

You will also find the almost ubiquitous *Brym capillare* (Capillary Thread-moss) which can inhabit most types of surface. Notice the many cylindrical dropping capsules.

*The ubiquitous **Bryum capillare**, Capillary Thread-moss, with short pale hairs projecting from the leaf tip. The capsules droop on long red stalks. This moss twists into a spiral when dry.*

*The bases of trees are often luxuriant in their covering of **Hypnum cupressiforme**, Cypress-leaved Plait-moss, which is coloured from mainly green to yellow to browns. It is easily recognised as the leaves curve downwards like the legs of a centipede.*

For more information on bryophytes

If you want to know more about mosses and liverworts the New Naturalist (97) *Mosses and Liverworts* by Ron Porley and Nick Hodgetts (2005) gives a good overview of British bryophytes and is very interesting and accessible. *British Mosses and Liverworts – a Field Guide* produced by the British Bryological Society and edited by Ian Atherton, Sam Bosanquet and Mark Lawley (2010) is an excellent start to identifying bryophytes. The British Bryological Society website has huge amounts of information on bryophytes, including local meetings and courses on bryophyte identification at this web address http://www.britishbryologicalsociety.org.uk/. You will find the name and contact details of the local Bryophyte Recorder on the website. There is also a Facebook page where experts can help identify your bryophytes.

Bryophytes of Toton Sidings (February 2018)

Common name	Scientific name	Bryophyte group
Creeping Feather-moss	*Amblystegium serpens*	moss
Lesser Bird's-claw Beard-moss	*Barbula convoluta*	moss
Bird's-claw Beard-moss	*Barbula unguiculata*	moss
Rough-stalked Feather-moss	*Brachythecium rutabulum*	moss
Red Beard-moss	*Bryoerythrophyllum recurvirostrum*	moss
Silver-moss	*Bryum argenteum*	moss
Capillary Thread-moss	*Bryum capillare*	moss
Bicoloured Bryum	*Bryum dichotomum*	moss
Crimson-tuber Thread-moss	*Bryum rubens*	moss
Pointed Spear-moss	*Calliergonella cuspidata*	moss
Heath Star Moss	*Campylopus introflexus*	moss
Common Threadwort	*Cephaloziella divaricata*	liverwort
Redshank	*Ceratodon purpureus*	moss
Hair-pointed Feather-moss	*Cirriphyllum piliferum*	moss
Lateral Cryphaea	*Cryphaea heteromalla*	moss
Silky Forklet-moss	*Dicranella heteromalla*	moss
Field Forklet-moss	*Dicranella staphylina*	moss
Broom Fork-moss	*Dicranum scoparium*	moss
Cylindric Beard-moss	*Didymodon insulanus*	moss
Common Striated Feather-moss	*Eurhynchium striatum*	moss
Lesser Pocket-moss	*Fissidens bryoides var. bryoides*	moss
Common Pocket-moss	*Fissidens taxifolius var. taxifolius*	moss
Dilated Scalewort	*Frullania dilatata*	liverwort
Grey-cushioned Grimmia	*Grimmia pulvinata*	moss
Silky Wall Feather-moss	*Homalothecium sericeum*	moss
Cypress-leaved Plait-moss	*Hypnum cupressiforme var. cupressiforme*	moss
Supine Plait-moss	*Hypnum cupressiforme var. resupinatum*	moss
Heath Plait-moss	*Hypnum jutlandicum*	moss
Common Feather moss	*Kindbergia praelonga*	moss
Forked Veilwort	*Metzgeria furcata*	liverwort
Wood Bristle-moss	*Orthotrichum affine*	moss
Anomalous Bristle-moss	*Orthotrichum anomalum*	moss
White-tipped Bristle-moss	*Orthotrichum diaphanum*	moss
Elegant Bristle-moss	*Orthotrichum pulchellum*	moss
Swartz's Feather-moss	*Oxyrrhynchium hians*	moss
Cuspidate Earth-moss	*Phascum cuspidatum var. cuspidatum*	moss
Taper-leaved Earth-moss	*Pleuridium acuminatum*	moss
Nodding Thread-moss	*Pohlia nutans*	moss
Juniper Haircap	*Polytrichum juniperinum*	moss
Hornschuch's Beard-moss	*Pseudocrossidium hornschuchianum*	moss
Neat Feather moss	*Pseudoscleropodium purum*	moss
Even Scalewort	*Radula complanata*	liverwort
Clustered Feather-moss	*Rhynchostegium confertum*	moss
Springy Turf-moss	*Rhytidiadelphus squarrosus*	moss
Thickpoint Grimmia	*Schistidium crassipilum*	moss
Lesser Yoke-moss	*Zygodon conoideus*	moss

Fungi

Fungi are a wide class of organisms, which are found in many areas. Those in Toton can be seen in many habitats, on trees, on rotting logs, in the leaf litter and on the ground. They are varied in form, size and shape and are an important part of the ecosystem. Some fungi can break down wood, helping the process of decomposition. They can also recycle and create nutrients in the soil which helps plants to grow and thrive. Some fungi (mushrooms) are edible but others are poisonous and some fungus cause disease in plants and animals (e.g Ash die back disease, Foot rot in sheep).

Examples of fungus on trees

Willow bracket fungus

Woodwart

Silver leaf fungus

Variations in willow fungus are currently causing confusion and under scrutiny for precise identification.

Mazegill fungus nestles in the trunks.

Fungi growing on the ground or in leaf litter

Blushing Dapperling

Common ink cap

Pestle Puff ball

Earth Ball fungus

The order of fungi is by common names if available. Families such as Field mushroom and wood mushroom have been put together. Some specimens are difficult to identify and some can only be identified under a microscope. Spp means species type.

Common Name	Scientific/latin name	Notes or nicknames
Big Smoky bracket	Bjerkandera adusta	
Birch Polypore	Piptiporus betulina	
Bleached brittle gill	Russula exalbicans	
Blushing bracket	Daealeopsis confragosa	Pore layer bruises when pressed *on willow or birch*
Blushing Dapperling	Leucoagaricus Badhamii	
Blushing Rosette	Abortiporus biennis	
Boot lace/honey fungus	Armillaria mellea	
Brown Birch Boletas	Laccium scabrum	
Orange Birch Boletas	Laccium versipelle	
Clouded funnel	Clitocybe nebularis	Grows in clusters and rings
Common ink cap	Coprinus atramentorius	
Common Jelly Spot	Dacrymyces stillatus	Grows on rotting wood
Common mazegill	Datronia mollis	
Coral Spot	Nestris cinnabarins	Found on dead deciduous branches
Deadman's Fingers	Xylaria polymorphs	
Dryad's saddle	Polyporus squamosus	
Dyeball	Pisolithus Arhizus	
Ergot	Claviceps purpurea	*St Antony's fire medieval poison – highly poisonous*
Field Blewit	Lapita saeva	Found grassland September to January
Wood Blewit	Lapita nuda	Found by hedgerows, woodlands
Field Mushroom	Agaricus campestris	
Wood mushroom	Agaricus sylvaticus	
Fly Agaric	Amanita muscaria	Bright red poisonous toadstool with white gills
Jelly Ear	Auricularia aurioula -judea	
King Alfreds cakes	Daldinia concentrica	*Coal fungus, cramp balls* Found on Ash trees
Pestle Puff-Ball	Lycoperdon excipliforme	
Scaly earth ball	Scleroderma verrucosum	
Shaggy Parasol	Lepiota rhacodes	Found on lawns, waste places, roadsides
Shaggy Ink Cap	Coprinus comatus	*Lawyers wig mushroom*
Common Ink cap	Coprinus atramentarius	
Silver Leaf fungus	Chondrostereum purpurea	
Summer Truffle	Tuber aestrivum	Found with Beech trees
Turkey Tail	Trametes	
	Coriolus zonata	Infrequent annual with overlapping brackets
	Gymnopilus spp	
	Hypholoma marginatum?	
	Leucoagaricus Badhamii	
Willow bracket	Phellinus igniarius	Common perennial on willow
	Psathyrella spp	
	Piptiporus betulina	
Woodwart	Hypoxylon fuscum?	

Turkey tail fungus among ivy

clouded funnel among hawthorn leaves

Lawyers wig

Conclusion

It can be seen that the diverse habitats of the area support a wide range of flora and fauna. It has been very pleasing to see and record some species which are of county or even national importance. Among these one has to comment on the presence of seven species of bat, all of which are protected species.

While many of the plants are considered by some folk as weeds in our gardens, they do support many pollinating insects and are a necessary part of the ecosystem. It is pleasing to see that among the data collected there are a few rarities amongst the flowers, butterflies moths, and hoverflies. A sighting of the Longhorn beetle was particularly rewarding as it is on the "red" list.

Work continues to improve the landscape for people and wildlife, some of which has been funded by the Tesco "bags" scheme. March 2018 saw new ponds dug with the aim of attracting more wild creatures. The old ones could not be enlarged as frogspawn had already been laid. These new ponds will hopefully attract a wider, more diverse range of species such as dragonflies, whirligig beetles, pond skaters and other invertebrates. It is hoped the amphibians will enjoy the greater space and maybe attract other types, maybe newts? The Tesco fund also enabled improvement to footpaths, allowing for wheelchair access. New notice boards have been erected.

The writing of this book has involved many members of Friends of Toton Fields which was formed in 2008. The first project of this group was the creation of Toton Fields Local Nature Reserve. Since then much has been achieved in cooperation with the Broxtowe Borough Council, local residents, and experts, who all give their time and knowledge freely.

If you have enjoyed this book, please consider helping Friends of Toton Fields in their quest to maintain, preserve and save at least some part of Toton from urbanisation and concrete with the resulting pollution, air noise, litter etc. The group carries out at least two litter picks every year and with more help can organise other events on topics mutually beneficial to wildlife and people.

For further information please contact Friends of Toton Fields or ask at Toton Library.